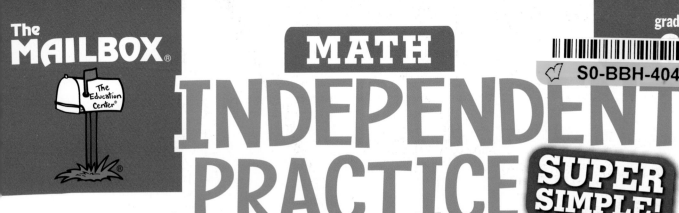

# The MAILBOX®

The Education Center®

grade

S0-BBH-404

# MATH
# INDEPENDENT PRACTICE
## SUPER SIMPLE!

## 144 EASY-TO-USE IDEAS FOR SKILL REINFORCEMENT

✓ Addition & subtraction

✓ Multiplication & division

✓ Number sense

✓ Patterns

✓ Measurement

✓ Geometry

✓ Data analysis

✓ AND LOTS MORE!

## ENOUGH FOR
## 4 activities for every week
## OF THE SCHOOL YEAR

**Managing Editor:** Hope Taylor Spencer

**Editorial Team:** Becky S. Andrews, Diane Badden, Amber Barbee, Cindy Barber, Amy Barsanti, Brooke Beverly, Tricia Brown, Kimberley Bruck, Karen A. Brudnak, Pam Crane, Chris Curry, Colleen Dabney, Lynette Dickerson, Bonnie Gaynor, Tazmen Hansen, Marsha Heim, Lori Z. Henry, Cynthia Holcomb, John Hughes, Laura Johnson, Jennifer L. Kohnke, Theresa Lewis Goode, Debra Liverman, Dorothy C. McKinney, Thad H. McLaurin, Geoff Mihalenko, Laura Mihalenko, Sharon Murphy, Jennifer Nunn, Jennifer Otter, Jenice Pearson, Mark Rainey, Greg D. Rieves, Hope Rodgers, Rebecca Saunders, Kathleen Scavone, Donna K. Teal, Joshua Thomas, Zane Williard

# www.themailbox.com

©2008 The Mailbox® Books
All rights reserved.
ISBN10 #1-56234-847-7 • ISBN13 #978-156234-847-2

Except as provided for herein, no part of this publication may be reproduced or transmitted in any form or by any means, electronic or mechanical, including photocopying, recording, or storing in any information storage and retrieval system or electronic online bulletin board, without prior written permission from The Education Center, Inc. Permission is given to the original purchaser to reproduce patterns and reproducibles for individual classroom use only and not for resale or distribution. Reproduction for an entire school or school system is prohibited. Please direct written inquiries to The Education Center, Inc., P.O. Box 9753, Greensboro, NC 27429-0753. The Education Center®, The Mailbox®, the mailbox/post/grass logo, and The Mailbox Book Company® are registered trademarks of The Education Center, Inc. All other brand or product names are trademarks or registered trademarks of their respective companies.

Manufactured in the United States
10 9 8 7 6 5 4 3 2 1

# Table of Contents

To use the table of contents as a checklist, make a copy of pages 2 and 3. Staple or clip each copy on top of its original page. Each time you use an activity, check its box. Start each school year with fresh copies of the pages.

**Skills Index on pages 111-112.**

## All in a Line

### Ordering numbers

**Materials:**
deck of cards with the face cards removed
paper strips (ten per student)
paper

Explain to students that each ace equals "1." To make a four-digit number, a child draws four cards and records on a strip the numbers in the order drawn. He repeats the steps nine times to create a total of ten strips. Then he arranges the strips in order from least to greatest and records the numbers on his paper.

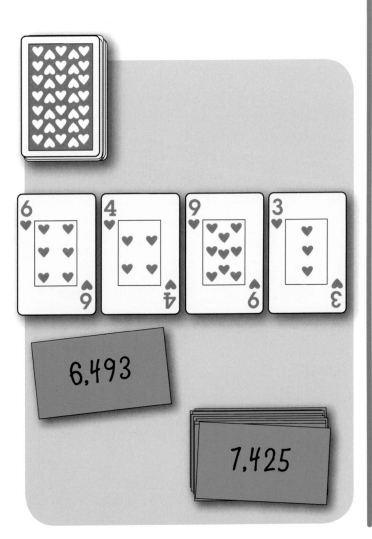

## Three in a Row!

### Addition facts

For partners

**Materials:**
deck of cards
paper

One partner shuffles the cards and stacks them facedown in two piles. The other partner draws a tic-tac-toe board on a sheet of paper. Each player then turns over his top two cards and finds the sum of the numbers. If one card is a face card, it takes the value of the other card. If both cards are face cards, the player chooses each card's value (up to 10). The player with the larger sum draws his mark in a space on the gameboard. If both sums are the same, each player draws another card and adds it to his sum. Play continues until one player wins by drawing three marks in a horizontal, vertical, or diagonal row, or until the gameboard is filled and a tie is declared.

## Day by Day

### Calendar

**Materials:**
student copies of page 76
calendar for current month

A child uses the calendar to complete the activity.

## Money Matters

### Counting coins

**Materials:**
cards programmed with various money amounts
coin manipulatives
paper

A child takes a card and records the money amount on his paper. Then he uses the manipulatives to make two different coin combinations that each equal the amount. On his paper, he draws the combinations and then circles the one that uses the least number of coins. He repeats the steps as time allows. For an added challenge, the child revisits each amount and uses the manipulatives to try to make coin combinations that use fewer coins than the circled combination.

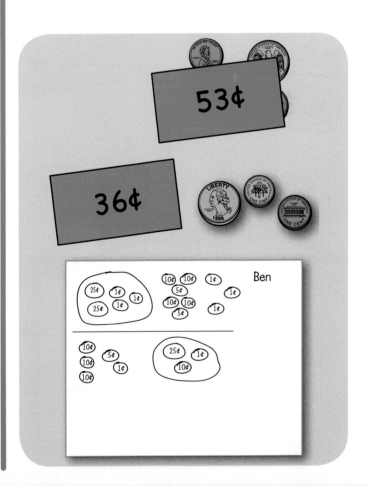

## Sorting It Out

### Odd and even numbers

**Materials:**
number cards
2 envelopes, labeled as shown
paper

A student draws a card, decides whether the number is odd or even, and places the card in the matching envelope. She continues until she has sorted all the cards. Then she empties the envelopes and copies the numbers in two columns on her paper.

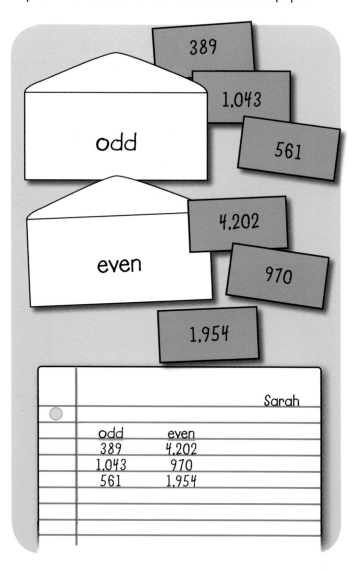

## Card Connections

### Fact practice

**Materials:**
copy of page 77, cut apart
3 cards programmed with math symbols: +, –, =
paper

A child arranges three number cards and two symbol cards into an addition or subtraction sentence and then writes the sentence on his paper. He repeats these steps as time allows. For an added challenge, the child writes the related addition or subtraction fact next to each fact he has written.

Sam

9 + 7 = 16

13 – 5 = 8

## During My Day

### Time

**Materials:**
student copies of the clock patterns on page 78
6" construction paper squares (seven per child)
glue
scissors
stapler
crayons

A student draws hands on each clock face to represent time of day. Next, she cuts apart the clocks and glues each one on a different paper square. On each square, she writes and illustrates a sentence about something she does at that time during her day. To create a booklet, she stacks the pages in order behind a cover and staples the pages together.

## Mixing It Up

### Addition without regrouping

**Materials:**
4 cards, each programmed with a different number from 2–5
paper

A child uses the numbers on the cards to make a two-digit addition problem. He writes and solves the problem on his paper. He continues rearranging, recording, and solving problems as time allows.

Tom

| | | | |
|---|---|---|---|
| 23 | 23 | 24 | 24 |
| + 45 | + 54 | + 35 | + 53 |
| 68 | 77 | 59 | 77 |
| 25 | 25 | 32 | 32 |
| + 34 | + 43 | + 45 | + 54 |
| 59 | 68 | 77 | 86 |
| 34 | 34 | 43 | 42 |
| + 25 | + 52 | + 52 | + 35 |
| 59 | 86 | 95 | 77 |
| 42 | 54 | 45 | 35 |
| + 53 | + 23 | + 32 | + 42 |
| 95 | 77 | 77 | 77 |
| 52 | | | |
| + 34 | | | |
| 86 | | | |

## All in the Family

### Fact families

**Materials:**
number cards labeled with the following numbers:
   *7, 3, 10, 6, 5, 11, 5, 9, 14, 8, 7, 15*
paper

A child arranges the cards into four groups so there is one sum and its two addends in each group. Then the child writes on his paper an addition fact for each group. Under each fact, he writes the remaining facts in the family as shown. For an added challenge, have the child repeat the activity with three additional cards.

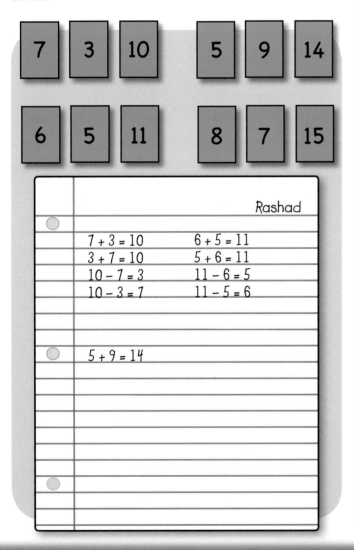

## Folding Flowers

### Time

**For partners**

**Materials:**
student copies of the flower gameboard
   on page 79, cut out
copy of the clock cards on page 79, cut apart
time list (see below)

Each player writes a different time from the list on each of her flower's petals. One player shuffles the cards, places the deck facedown, and turns over the first card. If she has on her flower the time shown on the card, she folds back the matching petal and her turn is over. If the time is not on her flower, her turn is over. Her partner takes a turn in the same manner. The first player to fold back every petal on her flower wins.

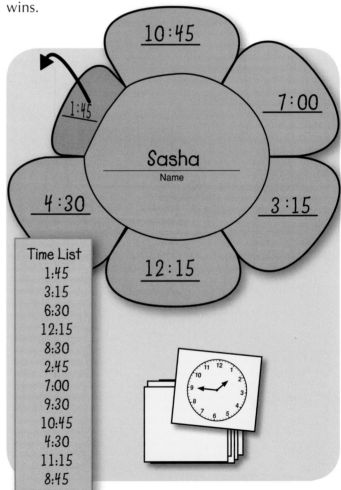

# From Lowest to Highest

## Ordering numbers

**Materials:**
cards programmed with four-digit numbers,
    placed in a gift bag
paper

A student takes the number cards out of the gift bag and orders them from lowest to highest. Then he copies the numbers on his paper.

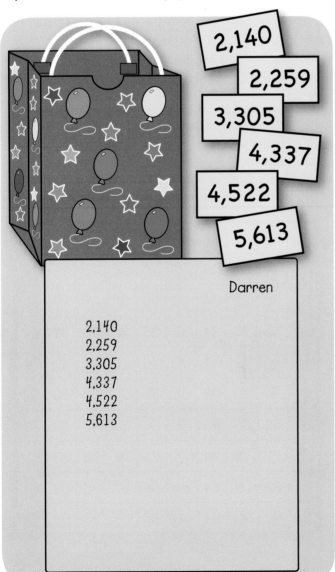

2,140

2,259

3,305

4,337

4,522

5,613

Darren

2,140
2,259
3,305
4,337
4,522
5,613

# Add It to 38!

## Addition with regrouping

**Materials:**
card labeled "38"
pair of dice
paper

A child copies the number from the card onto her paper. She rolls the dice and writes the resulting two-digit number under the number 38 to create an addition problem. After solving the problem, she repeats the steps as time allows.

38

Helen

| 38 | 38 | 38 |
|----|----|----|
| + 23 | + 64 | + 35 |
| 61 | 102 | 73 |

38
+ 11
____

## Rolling Along

### Time

**Materials:**
student copies of the clock patterns on page 78
clock with manipulative hands
pair of dice
paper
scissors
glue

A child rolls the dice and then sets the minute hand of the clock on the number that is rolled. He rolls the dice again, sets the hour hand on the resulting number, and then adjusts the minute hand to reflect the time. He draws the hands on a clock pattern, cuts out the clock pattern, and glues it on his paper. Then he writes the time below the clock. He repeats the steps as time allows.

## Four in a Row

### Odd and even numbers

**For partners**

**Materials:**
deck of cards with the face cards removed
copy of the hundred chart on page 78 (one per pair of students)
2 different-colored markers
highlighter

Explain to students that each ace equals "1." Each player chooses a marker. One partner shuffles the cards, places the deck facedown, and then turns over the top card. If it is an odd number, he makes a dot on an odd number on the chart. If it is an even number, he makes a dot on an even number. Players take turns in this manner. Each time a player marks four squares in a row either horizontally, vertically, or diagonally, he highlights the squares and earns a point. (Highlighted squares may not be used again.) Players play through the deck one time and then count their points. The player with the most points is declared the winner.

| 1 | 2 | 3 | 4 | 5 | 6 | 7 | 8 | 9 | 10 |
|---|---|---|---|---|---|---|---|---|---|
| 11 | 12 | 13 | 14 | 15 | 16 | 17 | 18 | 19 | 20 |
| 21 | 22 | 23 | 24 | 25 | 26 | 27 | 28 | 29 | 30 |
| 31 | 32 | 33 | 34 | 35 | 36 | 37 | 38 | 39 | 40 |
| 41 | 42 | 43 | 44 | 45 | 46 | 47 | 48 | 49 | 50 |
| 51 | 52 | 53 | 54 | 55 | 56 | 57 | 58 | 59 | 60 |
| 61 | 62 | 63 | 64 | 65 | 66 | 67 | 68 | 69 | 70 |
| 71 | 72 | 73 | 74 | 75 | 76 | 77 | 78 | 79 | 80 |
| 81 | 82 | 83 | 84 | 85 | 86 | 87 | 88 | 89 | 90 |
| 91 | 92 | 93 | 94 | 95 | 96 | 97 | 98 | 99 | 100 |

HIGHLIGHTER

## Two Views

### Place value

**Materials:**
student copies of page 80
cards programmed with three-digit numbers
paper
scissors
glue

A student draws a card. She cuts out place-value blocks that equal the number, glues them on her paper, and draws a box around the model. Then she cuts out place-value blocks to make a different combination of the same number and glues them next to the first model. She draws a box around the second model and labels both boxes with the number. She repeats the activity with the remaining cards.

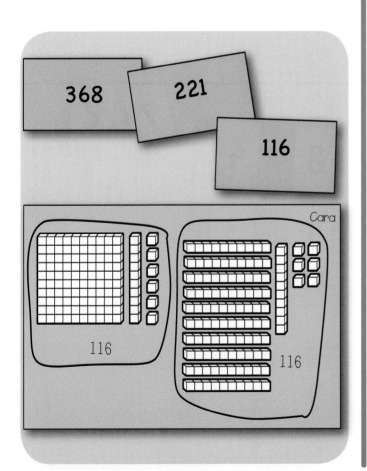

## Colorful Columns

### Addition with and without regrouping

**Materials:**
yellow construction paper strip labeled "hundreds"
green construction paper strip labeled "tens"
blue construction paper strip labeled "ones"
Unifix cubes
pair of dice
paper

A child arranges the strips to form three columns as shown. He rolls the dice and arranges Unifix cubes on the place-value columns to create the two-digit number shown. He rolls the dice again and creates a second number on the columns. Then he writes an addition problem on his paper using the two numbers. To solve the problem, he adds the cubes in the ones column and carries any tens into the tens column. Then he adds the cubes in the tens column, carrying any hundreds into the hundreds column. Finally, he writes the answer on his paper.

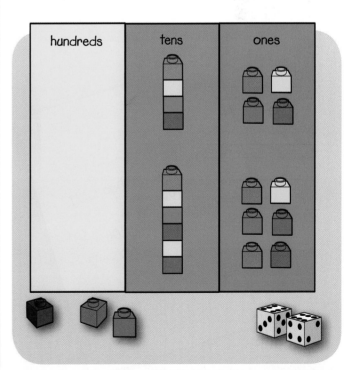

## Calling All Numbers

### Comparing numbers

**Materials:**
phone book pages
vocabulary list of inequality words
paper

A student circles two phone numbers on a page. She copies on her paper the last four digits of each number. Then she uses the numbers in sentences, using the vocabulary list as she writes. She repeats the activity with new numbers as time allows.

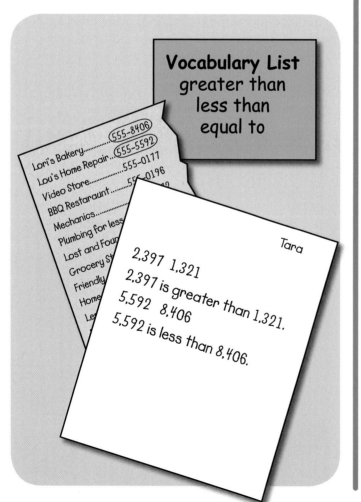

Vocabulary List
greater than
less than
equal to

Lori's Bakery............... 555-8406
Lou's Home Repair... 555-5592
Video Store................. 555-0177
BBQ Restaraunt......... 555-0196
Mechanics.....
Plumbing for less
Lost and Fou
Grocery St
Friendly
Home
Le

Tara

2,397  1,321
2,397 is greater than 1,321.
5,592  8,406
5,592 is less than 8,406.

## A Home For Numbers

### Addition with and without regrouping

**Materials:**
copy of the house pattern on page 81
copy of the lower number cards on page 77, cut out
paper

A student arranges the cards on the house to make an addition problem. He writes and solves the problem on his paper. Then he repeats the activity until he has written a desired number of problems.

tens    ones

8  4
1  3

7  2
0

Alex

$$\begin{array}{r} 84 \\ +13 \\ \hline 97 \end{array}$$

## Colorful Cubes

### Multiplication readiness

**Materials:**
Unifix cubes
paper

A child arranges stacks of Unifix cubes so that each stack has an equal number of cubes. Then she writes the multiplication problem her arrangement represents. She continues in this manner until she has written several problems.

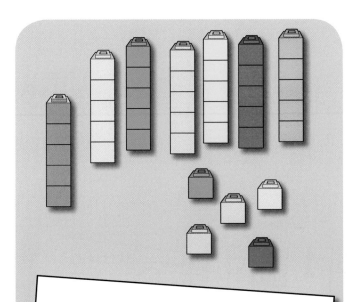

Samantha

$8 \times 4 = 32$

$7 \times 7 = 49$

$7 \times 5 = 35$

## What Time Is It?

### Time

**Materials:**
paper plates (one per child)
long and short paper clips (one of each per child)
time flash cards
marker
brads (one per child)
paper

A student uses a marker to draw a clock face on a paper plate. He straightens both his short and long paper clips and then uses the brad to attach them to the center of the plate. Next, he draws a flash card and arranges the hands on his clock to match the time shown. On his paper, he writes the time and two ways to say the time. He repeats the steps as time allows.

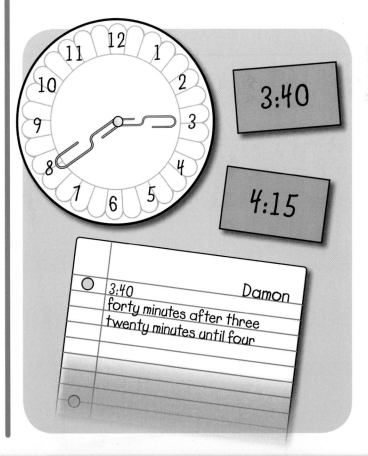

3:40

4:15

Damon

3:40
forty minutes after three
twenty minutes until four

# Set 6

## Places, Please!

### Ordering numbers

**Materials:**
copy of the lower number cards on page 77, cut apart
sticky notes (ten per child)
paper

A student arranges three cards into a number and then writes it on a sticky note. She repeats the steps to create nine more notes, arranges the notes in order from least to greatest, and copies the numbers on her paper. Then she writes sentences that tell which numbers are greater than and less than other numbers.

835  791  526  504

615  420  119  437

410

2 0 4
4 1 0

Kacey
119, 204, 410, 420, 437, 504,
526, 615, 791, 835

615 is greater than 204 but less than 791.
835 is greater than 615, 410, and 204.

## Classy Birthdays

### Graphs

**Materials:**
student copies of the tally chart on page 81
student copies of page 82
class birthday list

A child makes a mark on his tally chart to represent the birth month of each child in his class and then uses his tally chart to complete the bar graph. For an added challenge, the child writes on the back of his paper three questions about his graph. Then he writes the answers to his questions.

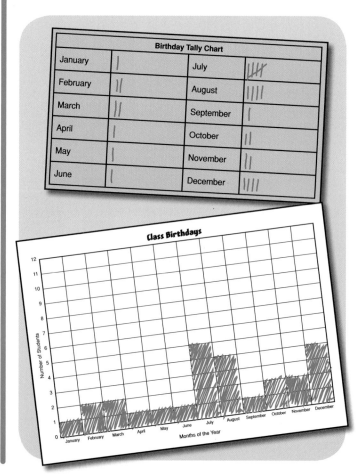

| Birthday Tally Chart | | | | |
|---|---|---|---|---|
| January | I | | July | IIII |
| February | II | | August | IIII |
| March | II | | September | I |
| April | I | | October | II |
| May | I | | November | II |
| June | I | | December | IIII |

Class Birthdays

## Dealing and Adding

### Patterns of ten

**Materials:**
copy of page 83, cut apart
copy of the hundred chart on page 78
paper

A child chooses a two-digit number card and a tens card. On her paper, she writes the numbers to create an addition problem, making sure to put the tens card as the second addend. Then she solves the problem, using the hundred chart to help her as needed. She repeats the activity as time allows.

## Picture a Product

### Multiplication readiness

**Materials:**
pair of dice
paper

A student rolls the dice and draws circles on his paper to equal the number shown on the dice. Then he rolls the dice again and draws in each circle dots to equal the number shown on the dice. He writes a multiplication problem that matches his picture and then repeats the activity as time allows.

## Quick Compare

### Comparing numbers

**For partners**

**Materials:**
2 copies of the place value mat on
   page 84, cut out
2 copies of the lower number cards on page 77,
   cut apart and combined into one deck
paper

Players take turns drawing cards until each
player has drawn four. Then each player arranges
his cards on his mat so that they form the largest
possible number. Players compare their numbers,
and the player with the higher one earns a point. Play
continues as time allows. The player with more points
at the end of the game wins.

## Keep Counting

### Number patterns

**Materials:**
copy of the two-digit number cards from
   page 83, cut apart
die
paper

To create a pattern, a child draws a card and writes
the number on her paper. She rolls the die, adds the
number rolled to the number she has written, and
writes the new number. She rolls the die again, adds
the number rolled to the new number, and then writes
the sum. Then she extends the pattern by writing the
next four numbers.

## Tackling Tasks

### Time to the minute

**Materials:**
copy of the task cards on page 84, cut out
clock
die
paper

A child takes one task card. She looks at the clock, writes the exact time, and begins the task. Once she has completed the task, she looks at the clock again and writes the time. Then she repeats the steps with the remaining cards. For an added challenge, the child writes the time that elapsed while completing each task.

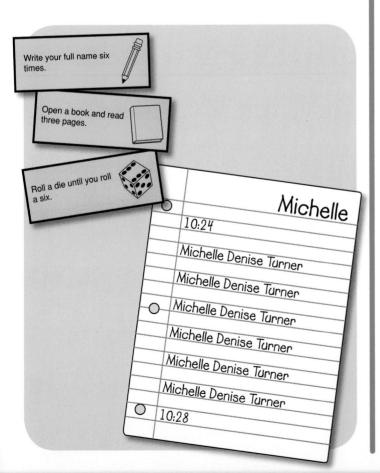

## What's Cooking?

### Subtraction with and without regrouping

**Materials:**
magnetic tape pieces labeled with numbers 0 to 9
metal cookie sheet
paper

A student chooses four numbers and arranges them on the cookie sheet to form a subtraction problem. Then he copies and solves the problem on his paper. He continues in this manner until he has copied and solved a desired number of problems.

## Counting in Cartons

### Multiplication readiness

**Materials:**
sanitized egg carton
beans
multiplication flash cards
paper

A student draws a flash card, looks at the second factor, and counts a matching number of beans into an egg cup. He continues in this way until he has beans in the same number of egg cups as the first factor. Then he writes and solves the multiplication problem on his paper, pouring out the beans and counting them for help. He repeats the steps to solve other multiplication problems.

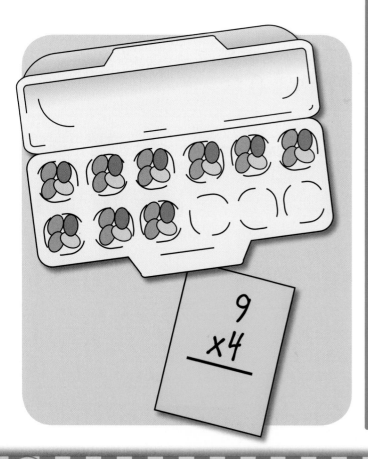

## Sorting Shapes

### Geometry

**Materials:**
graph paper
construction paper
ruler
scissors
glue

A child uses her ruler to draw several plane shapes on her graph paper. After cutting out the shapes, she labels each one with its number of angles. Next, she sorts her shapes according to their number of angles. Then she glues each set of shapes onto a separate sheet of construction paper and labels each grouping.

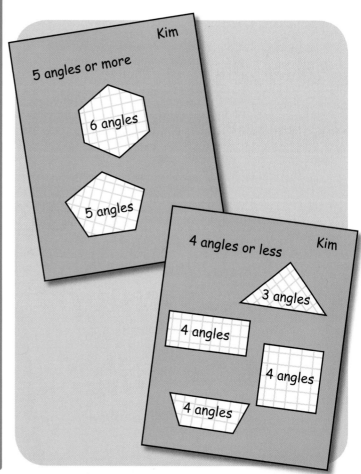

# Which Is Greater?

## Comparing numbers

**Materials:**
copy of the lower number cards on page 77, cut out
2 copies of the place value mat on page 84
paper

A child shuffles the cards and then deals four cards onto each place value mat, displaying them in the order they were dealt. She writes on her paper the resulting numbers and then writes the appropriate inequality symbol between them. She repeats the activity as time allows.

Liz

$5,439 < 8,102$
$6,283 > 4,957$
$7,192 > 3,850$

# A Shapely Lineup

## Geometric patterns

**Materials:**
die-cut plane shapes
paper

A student chooses two die-cut shapes and traces them on her paper so that they create a pattern. She extends the pattern across the page and then writes a sentence describing the pattern. Then she repeats the activity two additional times, making a different pattern each time. For an added challenge, the child creates a pattern using three die-cut shapes.

Brenda

My pattern is an abaa pattern.

## Up or Down?

### Rounding numbers

**Materials:**
copy of the spinner pattern on page 85,
    labeled with numbers 0–9
rounding code like the one shown
die
paper clip
pencil
paper

A child uses the pencil and paper clip to spin the spinner four times and writes the resulting four-digit number on his paper. He rolls the die, refers to the code to see how he should round the number, and then writes the rounded number on his page. The child repeats the steps as time allows.

Rounding Code
1, 2 = round to the nearest thousand
3, 4 = round to the nearest hundred
5, 6 = round to the nearest ten

Ben

9,640  9,600
3,108  3,110
7,492  7,000

## Dear Friend

### Addition with and without regrouping

**Materials:**
die
paper

A student rolls the die three times and writes the resulting three-digit number on her paper. Then she rolls the die three more times to create another number, writes it under the first number, and adds the numbers together. She repeats the steps until she has solved a predetermined number of problems. Next, she writes a letter to a classmate explaining how she knew whether or not to regroup as she completed the addition problems.

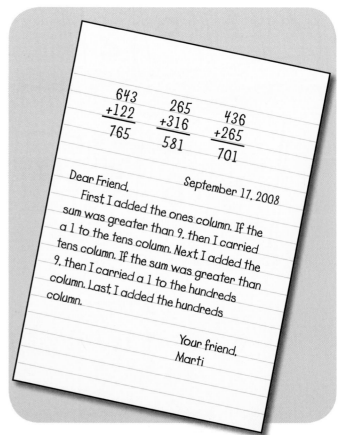

$$\begin{array}{r} 643 \\ +122 \\ \hline 765 \end{array} \qquad \begin{array}{r} 265 \\ +316 \\ \hline 581 \end{array} \qquad \begin{array}{r} 436 \\ +265 \\ \hline 701 \end{array}$$

September 17, 2008

Dear Friend,
    First I added the ones column. If the sum was greater than 9, then I carried a 1 to the tens column. Next, I added the tens column. If the sum was greater than 9, then I carried a 1 to the hundreds column. Last, I added the hundreds column.

           Your friend,
           Marti

## Perfect Timing

### Elapsed time

**Materials:**
paper lunch bag containing 5 labeled white cards:
    1:10, 4:30, 6:45, 8:05, 11:20
paper lunch bag containing 5 labeled colored cards:
    15 minutes, 30 minutes, 45 minutes,
    2 hours, 3 hours
clock with manipulative hands
paper

A student folds his paper into three equal sections, unfolds it, and then labels the resulting columns as shown. He draws a card from each bag and writes the time from the white card in the first column and the time increment from the colored card in the second column. Next, using the clock to help him, he finds the end time and writes it in the third column. The child repeats the steps with the remaining cards. If time allows, he puts the cards back in the bags, shakes the bags, and repeats the activity.

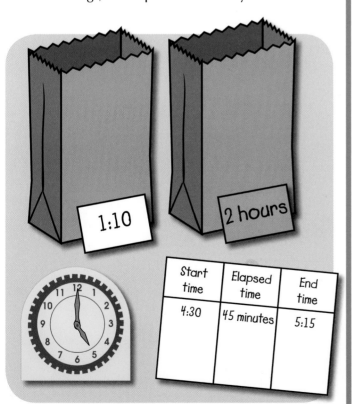

| Start time | Elapsed time | End time |
|---|---|---|
| 4:30 | 45 minutes | 5:15 |
| | | |

## Rolling for Shapes

### Geometry

For partners

**Materials:**
copy of the die pattern on page 86,
    labeled with shapes and assembled
2 Geoboards
rubber bands

One partner rolls the die and reads aloud the shape that is rolled. Each partner uses her bands to make the shape on her Geoboard. The partners compare their shapes and then remove the bands and repeat the activity.

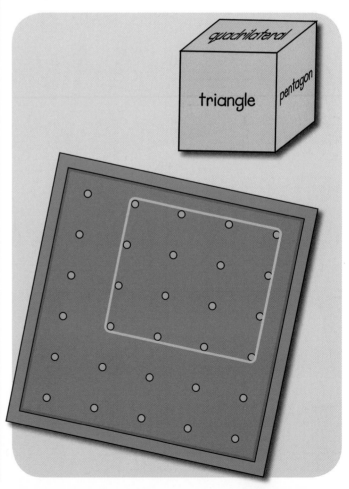

## Rows and Columns

### Multiplication readiness

**Materials:**
multiplication flash cards
graph paper
crayons

A student chooses a flash card and then colors on her graph paper an array that represents the multiplication problem. She writes and solves the problem under the array. Next, she writes on her graph paper the inverse of the problem and then colors an array that matches it. She compares the two arrays before she chooses a new flash card and repeats the activity.

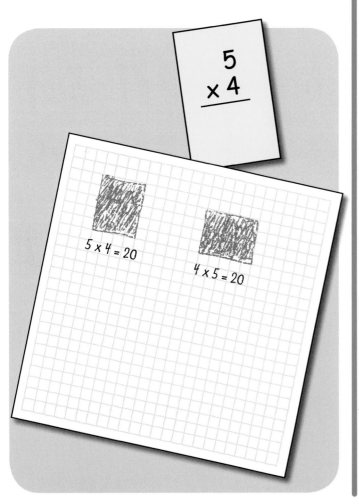

## Model Problems

### Addition without regrouping

**Materials:**
copy of the flash cards on page 85, cut out
place-value blocks
paper

A child draws a flash card and uses the place-value blocks to model and solve the problem. Then he copies on his paper the problem and its solution. He repeats the steps with the remaining cards.

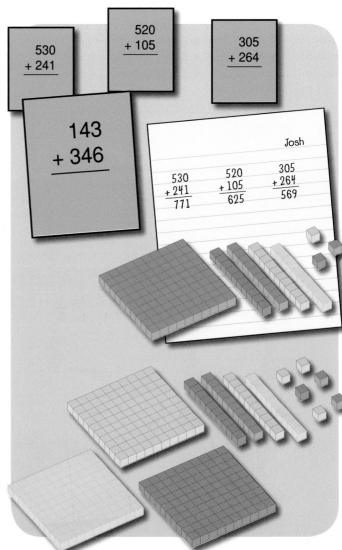

# Match a Measurement

## Length

**Materials:**
measurable items (such as a pencil, a textbook,
   a marker, and a dictionary)
cards (one for each item above, programmed
   with the item's height and width)
ruler

A child places each card on the object whose
measurement she thinks it matches and then uses the
ruler to check her guesses.

# Circle, Circle, Square

## Geometric patterns

**Materials:**
copy of page 87, cut out and assembled
paper

A student pulls the strips through the viewer until
they form a desired pattern and then copies it on her
paper. She extends the pattern by drawing the six
shapes that will come next. For an added challenge,
the child draws the shapes that come before the
pattern she has copied.

height = 11"
width = 8"

height = 1"
width = 8"

DRY-ERASE

Dana

## Spin Again!

### Expanded notation

**For partners**

**Materials:**
copies of page 88, cut out (one
   gameboard per student)
copy of the spinner on page 85,
   programmed with numbers 0–9
paper clip
pencil

One player uses the paper clip and pencil to spin the spinner. He writes the number in the first box on his gameboard. Then he spins the spinner five more times, writing each number in the order spun in the boxes of the first row. The second player takes a turn in a similar manner to fill the boxes of his first row. Then each player adds his numbers and writes the sum on the line. Players continue taking turns until both gameboards are filled in. Next, the players compare their gameboards and circle the higher sum in each row. The player with more circled sums is the winner.

## Measure Up

### Length

**Materials:**
items that can be measured to the nearest centimeter
ruler
paper

A child draws on her paper a three-column chart with headings as shown. She writes in the first column the name of one object, estimates its length, and writes the estimate in the second column. Then she measures the object and writes in the third column the actual measurement. She compares her estimate with the actual measurement and then, using the measurement of the first object to guide her, she repeats the steps with each of the remaining objects.

| object | estimate | measurement |
|---|---|---|
| envelope | 10cm | 9cm |

## Building Blocks

### Addition with and without regrouping

**Materials:**
centimeter graph paper
paper
scissors
glue

A student draws on her graph paper a box three columns wide and ten rows high. She randomly writes in each square a digit from 0 to 9 and then cuts the rows apart. She glues the rows on her paper to make five three-digit addition problems and then solves each problem.

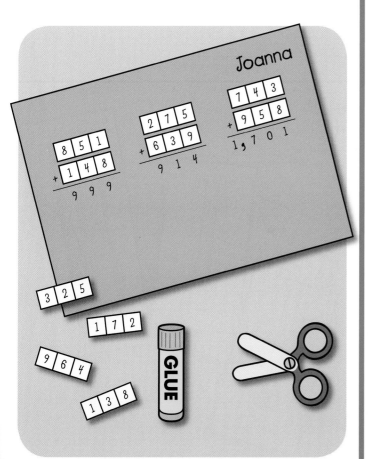

## Hop to the Product

### Multiplication readiness

**Materials:**
multiplication flash cards with products of 30 or less
centimeter ruler
paper

A child copies on his paper a multiplication fact. He places his ruler under the fact, putting his pencil point on the 0 mark. He "hops" (or skip-counts) his pencil to the number of centimeters represented by the second factor as shown. Then he keeps hopping until the number of hops equals the first factor. The number that his pencil lands on is the product that he writes on his paper. He continues in this manner with the remaining flash cards.

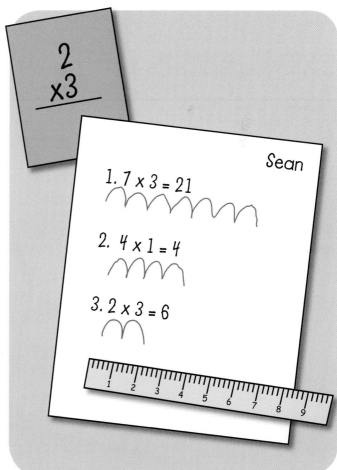

## Spin and Underline

### Place value

**Materials:**
cards labeled with four-digit numbers
copy of the spinner pattern on page 89, labeled as shown
paper clip
pencil
paper

A child chooses a card, copies the number onto her paper, and then uses the pencil and paper clip to spin the spinner. She writes the results of her spin and underlines the number that is in the place indicated by the spin. She repeats the steps as time allows.

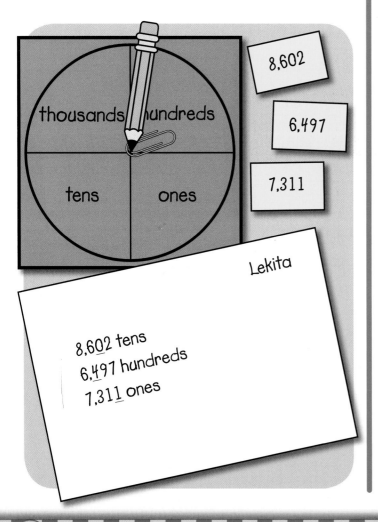

## How Hot? How Cold?

### Fahrenheit temperature

**Materials:**
student copies of page 90
cards labeled with different Fahrenheit temperatures
red crayon
scissors

A student colors half of the strip red. Then he cuts out the strip, thermometer, and thermometer cards. He cuts the slits in the thermometer and then threads the strip through the slits as shown. He draws a temperature card and then manipulates his thermometer until it matches the temperature shown on the card. Next, he copies the temperature onto a thermometer card and colors the thermometer to match his model. He repeats the activity as time allows.

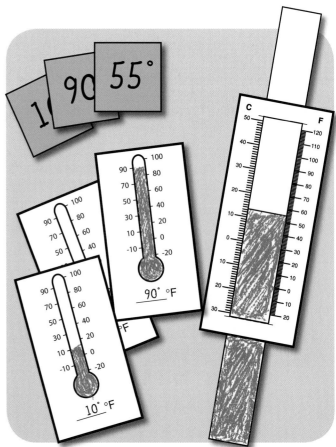

# Set 12

## Filling in the Gaps

### Ordering numbers

**Materials:**
cards labeled with the following numbers: 2,228;
2,738; 3,404; 5,713; 5,796; 7,603; 9,539; 9,642
paper

A student orders the cards from lowest to highest.
He copies the numbers onto his paper, leaving space
between each pair of numbers. Then, in each extra
space, he writes a number that comes between the
number pair.

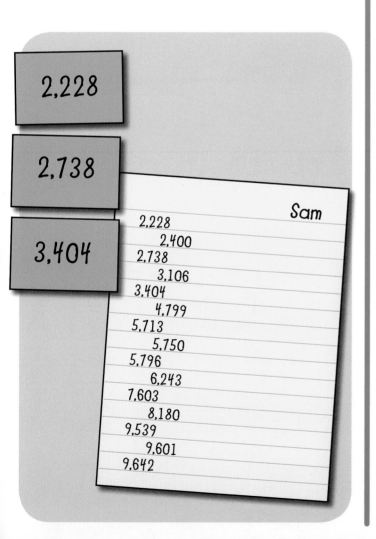

## Illustrating Facts

### Multiplication readiness

**Materials:**
multiplication flash cards
colored tiles
index cards
crayons
stapler

A student draws a flash card and then arranges
tiles to make an array that represents the fact on the
card. He draws the array on an index card and then
writes the fact below his drawing. To make a multiplication booklet, he makes several cards and then
staples them together.

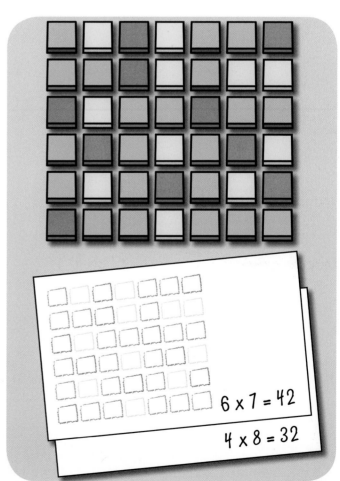

## Flip It!

### Basic facts

**Materials:**
2 sets of 10 cards, each card in a set labeled with a different number 1–10
pair of dice

For partners

Each player takes a set of cards and places them faceup in a row in front of him; then one player rolls the dice. He adds or subtracts the two numbers and flips over the card that matches the sum or difference. If he has already flipped the cards that match the sum and difference, his turn is over. If he rolls an 11, his partner must flip all his cards faceup. If a player rolls a 12, then he must flip all his own cards faceup. His partner takes a turn in the same manner. The first player to flip all his cards facedown is the winner.

## Are We There Yet?

### Length

**Materials:**
4½" x 6" construction paper rectangles (one per child)
ruler

A child draws a car in the upper left corner of her paper and then draws a small house in the lower right corner. She uses her ruler to measure and draw lines connecting the car to the house as shown. She adds the measurements together and writes the total on the back of her paper.

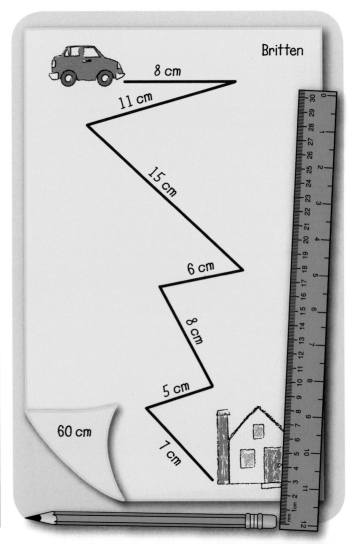

Britten

8 cm
11 cm
15 cm
6 cm
8 cm
5 cm
7 cm
60 cm

## Count and Sort

### Graphs

**Materials:**
a few small bags, each containing a group of items
   that can be sorted in 3–4 sets
graph paper
construction paper
crayons

Possible items to sort include colored tiles, buttons, game markers, and pom-poms.

A student empties one bag and its contents. Then she makes a graph that represents the contents of her bag. She cuts out the graph, mounts it on construction paper, and adds the appropriate titles.

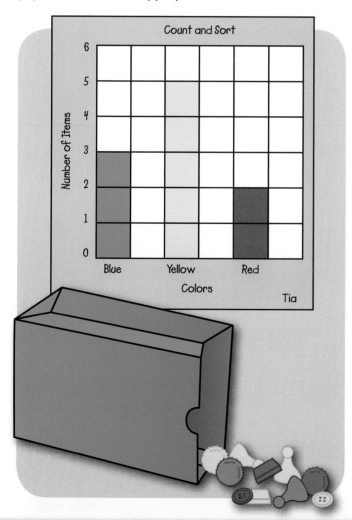

## All the Cards

### Addition with and without regrouping

For partners

**Materials:**
deck of playing cards with the face cards and tens removed
paper

One player shuffles the cards, cuts the deck in half, and then places the decks facedown. Each player takes a deck, turns over the top three cards, and arranges them in the order drawn to create a three-digit number. Then each player draws three more cards, creating a second three-digit number, and places those cards under the first number. He copies the numbers onto his paper, adds them together, and compares his sum to his partner's. The player with the higher sum takes all the cards. Play continues for two more rounds. The player who collects more cards is the winner.

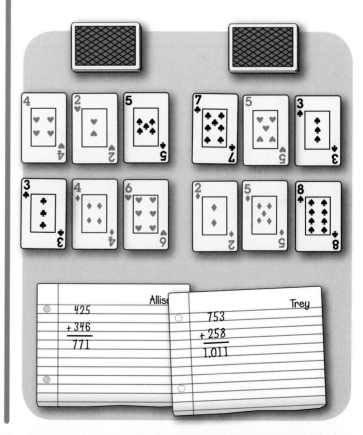

## Step by Step

### Expanded notation

**Materials:**
3" x 12" construction paper strips (three per child)

To make a booklet, a child stacks his strips, leaving one inch of each strip showing. Then he folds all three strips over until the top edge of the inside strip is one inch from the next strip. He staples the booklet on the fold. Next, he writes a six-digit number across the flaps as shown. To complete his booklet, he opens each flap and writes the expanded form information.

## Check It

### Multiplication

**Materials:**
multiplication flash cards
Geoboard
rubber bands
paper

A student draws a flash card and then copies and solves the problem. To check his answer, he wraps a rubber band around an array on the Geoboard that represents the problem. Then he counts the pegs that are inside the band and compares the total to his answer. He repeats the steps until he has written and checked a predetermined number of problems.

# Home Builder

## Length

**Materials:**
12" x 18" construction paper (one sheet per child)
ruler

A student folds her paper in half horizontally and keeps the paper folded. Starting at the fold line, she uses her ruler to draw half of a house, writing each line's measurement next to it, as shown. Then she unfolds the paper and, using her ruler and the measurements she has written to guide her, she draws the other half of the house.

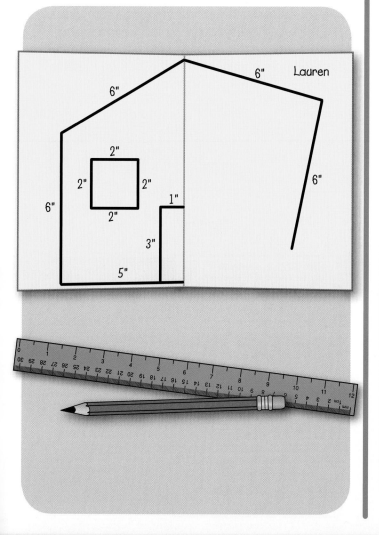

# Weather Wear

## Temperature

**Materials:**
student copies of the thermometer patterns on page 89
$4\frac{1}{2}$" x 6" paper pieces
scissors
glue
crayons

A student colors a thermometer to represent a desired temperature. Then she cuts out the thermometer and glues it on her paper. She draws on the paper clothing that would be appropriate to wear when it is that temperature. She repeats the steps with different temperatures until she has made a desired number of pages. To make a weather booklet, she stacks the pages behind a blank page, staples the stack along its edge, and then titles and decorates the cover.

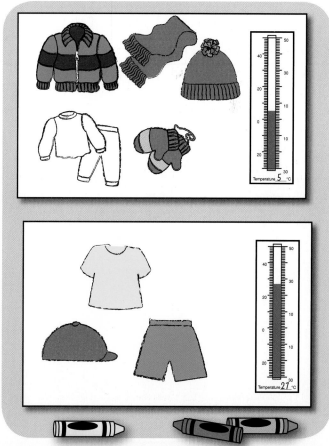

## What's in a Shape?

### Geometry

**Materials:**
student copies of page 91
Geoboards
rubber bands, red and green
crayons, red and green

A child uses a red rubber band to make a square, rectangle, or triangle on the Geoboard. Then he uses green rubber bands to make smaller shapes inside the larger shape. He uses the Geoboard and rubber bands as he completes the reproducible.

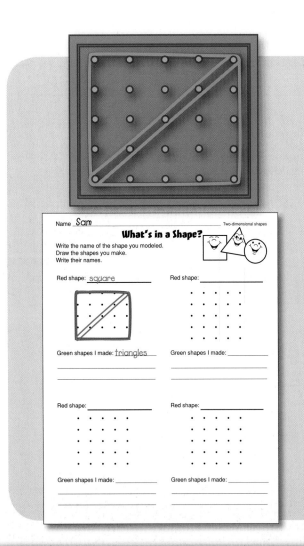

## Spin the Difference

### Subtraction without regrouping

**For partners**

**Materials:**
copy of page 92 (one per student pair)
2 copies of the spinner on page 85, labeled as shown
game markers
paper clip
pencil
paper

Each player places her game marker on Start. One player uses the pencil and paper clip to spin each spinner, writing the resulting numbers on her paper. Then she subtracts the smaller number from the larger one. The second player repeats the steps and the players compare their differences. The player with the larger difference moves her game marker ahead one space. Play continues until one player reaches Finish and is declared the winner.

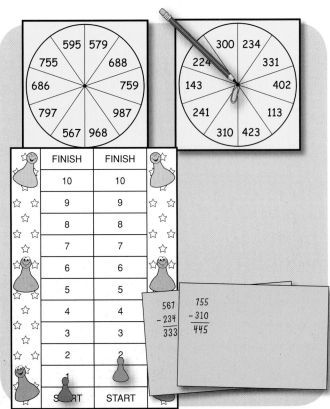

# Facts All Around

## Multiplication

**Materials:**
student copies of page 93 (two per child)
copy of the spinner on page 85, labeled and
    assembled as shown

A student spins the spinner and writes the number in the center of the top wheel. Next, he spins and writes numbers in the inner ring. Then he multiplies the center number by each number in the inner ring and writes each product in the outer ring. He completes each remaining wheel in the same manner without repeating numbers in the center of any wheels.

# What a Roundup!

## Rounding numbers

**Materials:**
2 place-value cards: tens, hundreds
number cards, each labeled with a different
    four-digit number
4' yarn length with its ends tied together
    to form a large circle
paper

A student spreads out the yarn circle and places the tens place-value card on it. Then he sorts the cards, placing those that round down to the nearest ten on the inside of the circle and those that round up to the nearest ten on the outside. He copies the rounded numbers in two columns, as shown, and repeats the steps with the hundreds place-value card.

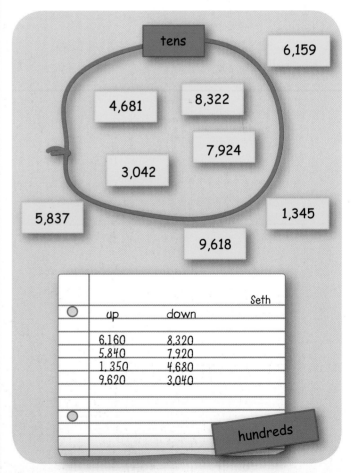

## Size It Up!

### Length

**Materials:**
several measurable items
centimeter ruler
paper

Possible items include a stapler, a pocket calendar, a drinking straw, a craft stick, and a pipe cleaner.

A child arranges the items from shortest to longest. Then he draws a simple drawing of the lineup of the objects. He measures each object to the closest centimeter and writes the measurement next to the object he has drawn.

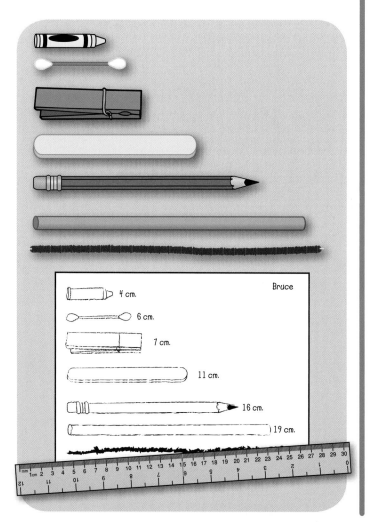

## A Shapely Robot

### Multiplication

**Materials:**
die-cuts of the shapes shown (several per child)
multiplication code like the one shown
construction paper
glue

A student arranges the die-cut shapes to create a robot shape on her paper. After gluing the shapes in place, she draws one of each shape on the back of her paper. She refers to the code as she completes multiplication facts about her picture as shown. For an additional challenge, replace the numbers on the code with higher numbers.

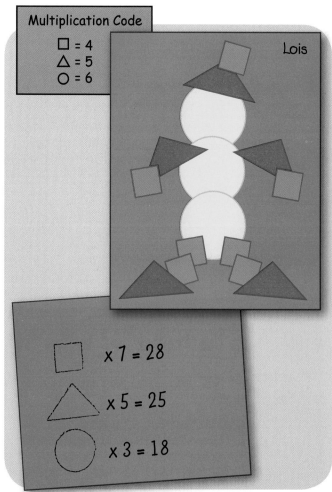

## Fruity Flavors

### Possible outcomes

**Materials:**
student copies of page 94
glue
scissors

A student follows the directions on the page to complete the activity.

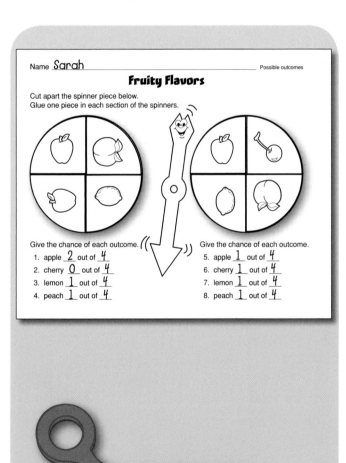

Name **Sarah**                                    Possible outcomes

**Fruity Flavors**

Cut apart the spinner piece below.
Glue one piece in each section of the spinners.

Give the chance of each outcome.
1. apple **2** out of **4**
2. cherry **0** out of **4**
3. lemon **1** out of **4**
4. peach **1** out of **4**

Give the chance of each outcome.
5. apple **1** out of **4**
6. cherry **1** out of **4**
7. lemon **1** out of **4**
8. peach **1** out of **4**

## Costly Words

### Adding three or more addends

**Materials:**
letter code like the one shown
posters labeled with different categories
scrap paper

Possible categories include pets, foods, color words, and sports.

On scrap paper, a child writes a word that matches one of the categories. Then he refers to the code as he writes, in a column, the value of each letter in his word. He adds the numbers together to find the total value of the word. Next, he copies the word on the matching poster, writing its value next to it. He continues adding words to the posters as time allows.

### Letter Code

| | |
|---|---|
| a = $6 | n = $2 |
| b = $4 | o = $6 |
| c = $3 | p = $7 |
| d = $7 | q = $1 |
| e = $2 | r = $5 |
| f = $9 | s = $9 |
| g = $1 | t = $4 |
| h = $5 | u = $7 |
| i = $8 | v = $1 |
| j = $4 | w = $8 |
| k = $7 | x = $2 |
| l = $3 | y = $6 |
| m = $8 | z = $3 |

Brandon

```
   5
   6
   8
   4
   2
 + 5
 ———
  39
```
hamster = $39

## Dotty Dominoes

### Subtraction with and without regrouping

**Materials:**
dominoes
paper

A child arranges three dominoes into a subtraction problem, as shown, making sure the domino in the hundreds place is flipped so the largest number is on top. Then he copies and solves the problem on his paper. He repeats the steps with different dominoes as time allows.

## Lift the Flap

### Number patterns

**Materials:**
4½" x 12" construction paper pieces
paper
scissors

For partners

To make a pattern strip, a child folds her paper in half lengthwise. Across the top flap, she makes seven cuts to the fold line about one inch apart. Next, she labels the top of each resulting flap as shown. Then she lifts each flap and writes a number pattern. On the back of the strip, the child writes the rule for her pattern. She repeats the steps to make several strips.

The child trades her strips with a partner. To use a pattern strip, the child lifts all the flaps except three. She copies the pattern on her paper and then fills in the missing numbers.

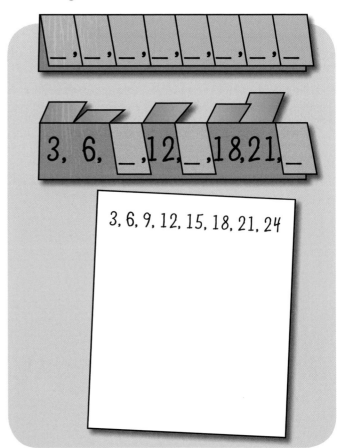

## Colorful Estimation

### Length

**Materials:**
different-colored ribbons, each measured
   and cut to different lengths

   A student writes on her paper the three headings shown. She chooses a ribbon, estimates its length, and writes the ribbon's color and her estimation under the corresponding headings. Then she measures the ribbon and writes the actual measurement. She repeats the steps with the remaining ribbons.

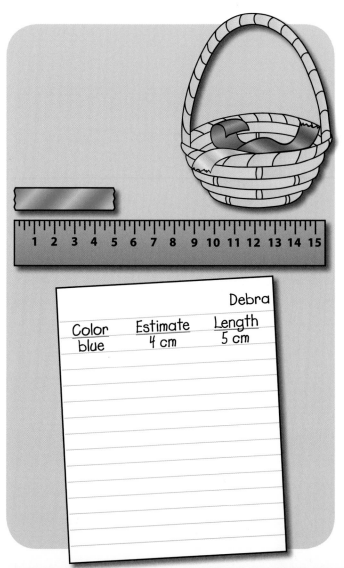

| | | Debra |
|---|---|---|
| Color | Estimate | Length |
| blue | 4 cm | 5 cm |

## A Shapely Comparison

### Geometry

**Materials:**
solid geometric figures, each labeled
   with a different number as shown
pair of dice
paper

   A child draws a simple Venn diagram on his paper. He rolls the dice and then picks up the two figures that match the numbers he rolled. (If doubles are rolled, the child rolls again until two different numbers are rolled.) He labels the diagram with the numbers and then completes the diagram. If time allows, he draws another Venn diagram on the back of his paper and repeats the activity.

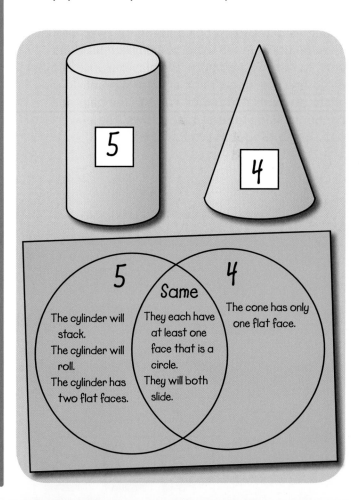

5 | Same | 4

The cylinder will stack.
The cylinder will roll.
The cylinder has two flat faces.

They each have at least one face that is a circle.
They will both slide.

The cone has only one flat face.

## Target Number

### Subtraction with and without regrouping

**For partners**

**Materials:**
copy of page 95, cut apart and sorted
    into 2 paper lunch bags labeled
    as shown
3 dice
blank cards
paper
2 calculators

One player rolls all three dice and uses them to make the smallest three-digit number he can. This becomes the target number. He writes the number on a blank card. Next, each player draws one number card from each bag and then writes and solves on his paper a subtraction problem using the two numbers. Then he uses his calculator to compare his difference to the target number. The player whose number is closer to the target number earns a point. To play again, students return their cards to the bags and continue taking turns as time allows. The player who earns the most points is the winner.

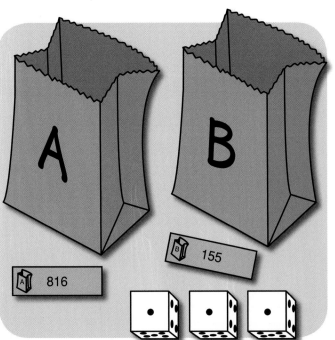

## Counting on Letters

### Frequency tables

**Materials:**
student copies of page 96
copy of a weekly spelling or vocabulary word list

A child writes each word from the list in the first column on her paper. She counts the number of consonants in the first word, making a tally mark in the second column for each one. Then she writes in the third column the total number of tally marks. She repeats the steps for each of the remaining words.

| Word | Tally Marks | Frequency |
|---|---|---|
| sour | II | 2 |
| round | III | 3 |
| pouch | III | 3 |
| thousand | HHI | 5 |
| surround | HHI | 5 |
| outside | III | 3 |
| snowplow | HHI I | 6 |
| clown | IIII | 4 |
| growl | IIII | 4 |
| flower | IIII | 4 |
| | | |
| | | |
| | | |
| | | |

# Roll One, Draw One

## Multiplication

**Materials:**
copy of the number cards from the top
    of page 77, cut apart
die
paper

A student shuffles the cards and then places the deck facedown. He rolls the die and then turns over the top card. He uses the resulting pair of numbers in a multiplication problem he writes on his paper. Then he solves the problem. He continues in this manner until he has written a problem using each of the remaining cards.

# Big Spender

## Adding money

For partners

**Materials:**
copy of the gameboard on page 92
two copies of page 97, cut apart
2 game markers
paper

Both players place their markers on "Start." One player shuffles the cards and places the deck facedown. Each player draws two cards and then uses the two numbers in an addition problem he writes and solves. The two players compare their sums, and the player with the higher sum moves his marker one space. Players continue taking turns in this manner. The first player to reach "Finish" wins the game. For an added challenge, the players repeat the activity, subtracting the money amounts instead of adding them.

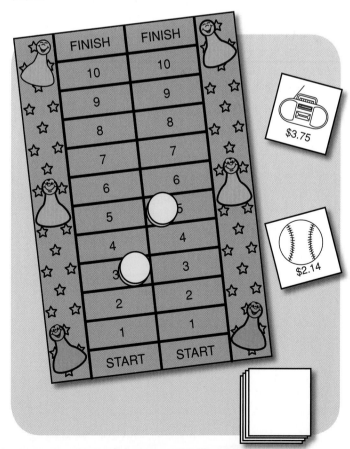

## Picture This!

### Multiplication

**Materials:**
colorful picture cards or magazine pages
multiplication flash cards
paper

A student chooses a picture and a flash card. Then he uses the picture for inspiration as he writes a story problem that matches the flash card. He continues in this manner until he has written a predetermined number of problems. On a separate page, the student writes the answers to his problems. If desired, collect the papers and then redistribute them so that another student solves the problems his classmate has written.

## Rolling for Cash

### Counting coins

For partners

**Materials:**
copy of 6 of the coin cards on page 98, cut out and glued on an assembled copy of the pattern on page 86
coin manipulatives

One player rolls the die and then takes the coin that is rolled. Her partner takes a turn in the same manner. Players continue taking turns, counting their coin totals as they play. If possible, players trade coins for other coins of equal value, such as five pennies for a nickel or five nickels for a quarter. The first player to reach a predetermined amount wins the game. For an added challenge, use different coin cards from page 98 to make a second die and have students play with two dice.

# Macaroni Math

## Associative property

**Materials:**
elbow macaroni
4½" x 6" blank cards (one per child)

On one card, the child writes a three-addend addition problem two times. In the first problem, she glues macaroni around the first two addends. In the second problem, she glues macaroni pieces around the second two addends. Then she solves both problems, using the macaroni parentheses to guide her as to which addends to add first. To complete the activity, she writes a sentence explaining what she notices about the two sums.

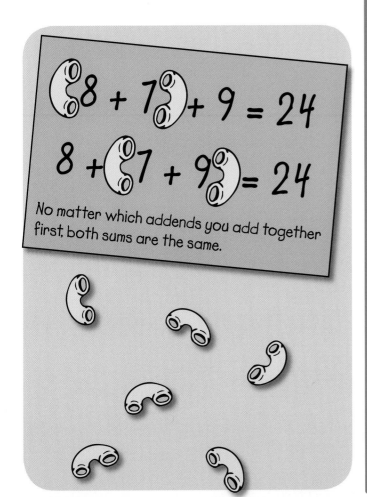

$$(8 + 7) + 9 = 24$$
$$8 + (7 + 9) = 24$$

No matter which addends you add together first, both sums are the same.

# How Long? How Tall?

## Length

**Materials:**
student copies of the reproducible on page 98
list of 8 classroom items and their measurements, similar to the one shown

A child uses the list to complete the activity on the reproducible.

door = 8 feet 3 inches

desk = 2 feet 4 inches

plant = 3 feet 8 inches

flag = 2 feet 2 inches

chair = 4 feet 1 inch

bookcase = 4 feet 7 inches

stool = 3 feet 5 inches

fan = 2 feet 0 inches

Standard measurement

Name _____

### How Long? How Tall?

Write the measurement of each item.
Then write each measurement in inches.
Use the table to help you.

| Feet | 1 | 2 | 3 | 4 | 5 | 6 | 7 | 8 |
|---|---|---|---|---|---|---|---|---|
| Inches | 12 | 24 | 36 | 48 | 60 | 72 | 84 | 96 |

| Item | Measurement | Measurement in Inches |
|---|---|---|
| door | 8 feet 3 inches | 99 inches |
| desk | 2 feet 4 inches | 28 inches |
| plant | 3 feet 8 inches | 44 inches |
| flag | 2 feet 2 inches | |
| chair | 4 feet 1 inch | |
| bookcase | 4 feet 7 inches | |
| | | |
| | | |

## Spending Spree

### Adding money

**Materials:**
student copies of page 97, cut apart
adding machine tape

A child writes "Receipt" at the top of a strip of adding machine tape. He chooses two item cards and writes on the tape the name and price of each item. He adds the prices together and then writes the sum on the tape. Then he chooses two different cards and repeats the steps. For an added challenge, the child chooses three items at a time to write on the tape.

## A Shapely Chain

### Geometric patterns

**Materials:**
2" x 9" paper strips
die-cut shapes (each smaller than 1" square)
    in a paper lunch bag
stapler

A student pulls a shape out of the bag and traces it on her strip. She repeats this step until she has created a four-unit pattern. Then she extends the pattern to the end of the strip. She continues in this manner until she has made a predetermined number of strips. Next, she uses a stapler to connect the strips into a paper chain.

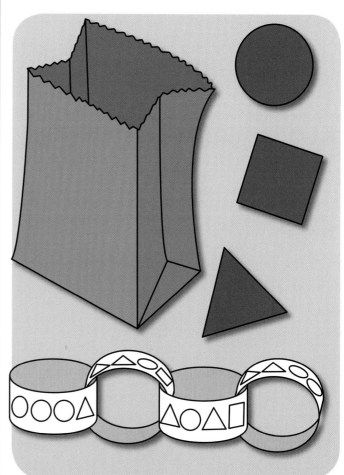

## Roll On!

### Subtraction with and without regrouping

**Materials:**
student copies of page 99
3 dice

A student uses the dice to complete the activity.

## Stamp It Out!

### Counting coins

**Materials:**
card labeled "89¢"
coin stampers
paper

A child fan-folds his paper to make horizontal rows about 1½" wide. Then he writes the amount from the card in the top row. In each of the remaining rows he stamps a different coin combination that equals the amount on the card. For additional practice, change the amount and have the child repeat the activity.

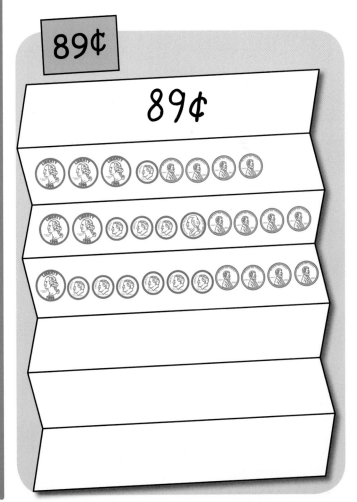

# Roll and Measure

## Length

**Materials:**
copy of the die pattern on page 86,
    assembled and labeled *inches, feet,*
    *yards, inches, feet, yards*
magazines
construction paper
scissors
glue

A child rolls the die and then writes on a sheet of construction paper the measurement unit rolled. Next, he cuts out a magazine picture of something that should be measured with that unit. Then he glues the picture to his paper and draws a box around the word and picture, as shown. He repeats the steps as time allows.

# On the Lookout

## Angles

**Materials:**
two 12" sentence strips, hole-punched and
    fastened with a brass fastener, as shown
    (one per child)
paper

A child draws on her paper a three-column chart with headings as shown. She uses the sentence strip angle to help her as she searches the classroom for examples of each type of angle. As she finds each example, she writes a note in the appropriate column to tell where the angle was found.

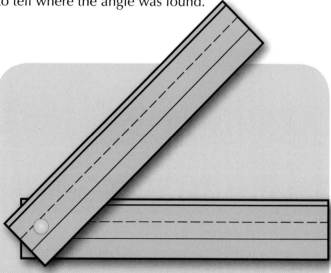

| acute angles | right angles | obtuse angles |
|---|---|---|
| | the cover of my book has right angles | the hands of the clock sometimes form an obtuse angle |

# Divided Equally

## Fractions

**Materials:**
6" x 9" paper pieces
stapler
crayons

A student looks around the classroom to find items—such as windows, bookcases, and file cabinets—that are divided into fractional parts. He draws each item on a separate piece of paper and then writes a sentence describing how the item is divided. To make a booklet, he stacks his completed pages, adds a cover page, and then staples the booklet together. He titles and decorates his booklet cover.

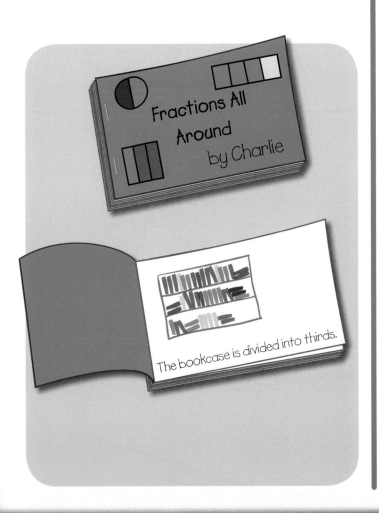

# Countdown

## Subtraction with and without regrouping

**Materials:**
card labeled "500"
deck of cards with the face cards and tens removed
paper

Explain to students that each ace equals one. A child draws two cards, arranges them to form a two-digit number (subtrahend), and writes a subtraction problem with 500 as the minuend. He continues drawing numbers and subtracting from the previous problem's difference until he draws a number that is larger than the last difference on his paper. He writes and circles the number of subtraction problems he has written. For an added challenge, the child repeats the activity, trying to arrange the cards he draws to form numbers that will help him reduce the number of subtraction problems he solves on his second attempt.

## Race to the Bank

### Counting money

**For partners**

**Materials:**
cards, each labeled with a different money amount
manipulative money

One player shuffles the cards, stacks them face-down, and turns over the top card. Each player races to count out money to equal the amount shown on the card. The first player to show the exact amount earns a point. Play continues as time allows. The player who earns more points is the winner.

## Mystery Number

### Missing addends

**Materials:**
2 copies of the spinner on page 85, labeled as shown
paper clip
pencil
paper

A student uses the pencil and paper clip to spin each spinner. Then he writes the numbers spun to create a missing addend problem, as shown. He solves the problem and repeats the steps to create another one. He continues as time allows.

## In Equal Sets

### Division readiness

**Materials:**
division flash cards
sanitized egg carton
beans
paper

A child draws a card and counts out beans to equal the dividend. She divides the beans equally into egg carton cups to represent the divisor. To find the quotient, she counts the beans in one cup. Then she writes the problem on her paper. She repeats the steps until she has written a desired number of problems.

## "Math-ercise"

### Computation

**Materials:**
cards, each labeled with a two-digit number
paper
calculator

A child draws a simple two-column chart on his paper. He takes ten cards and then writes the numbers from the cards in the first column. Next to each number, he writes an addition, subtraction, or multiplication fact that equals the number. Then he uses the calculator to check his work. For an added challenge, have the child draw a third column and then write in it an additional fact for each number.

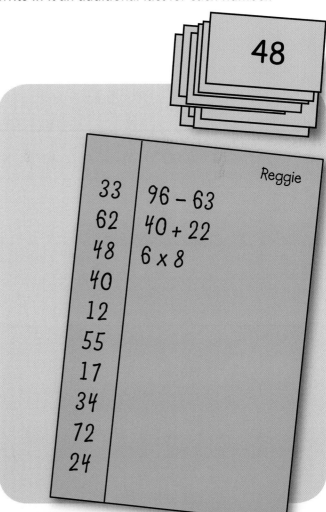

# Set 23

## Rolling for Factors

### Multiplication

**Materials:**
student copies of the bottom half of page 100
die

A child uses the die to complete the activity.

## Try Again!

### Congruence

For partners

**Materials:**
20 pairs of congruent die-cut shapes
2 folders
manilla envelope

One player puts all the shapes in the envelope and gently shakes it. Each player sets up his folder in front of him to act as a screen and then draws five shapes from the envelope. He lays his shapes out in front of him and sets aside any congruent pairs. One player holds up a shape and asks his opponent for the congruent shape. If his opponent has the match, the opponent gives it to him and his turn is over. If not, the player draws a shape from the envelope and his turn is over. Players continue taking turns in this manner until one player has matched all his shapes. The player who has more pairs is the winner.

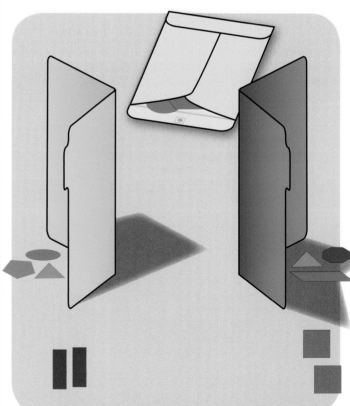

## Subtract Again

### Division readiness

**Materials:**
3 cards, each labeled with a different one of
   the following numbers: *24, 36, 48*
copy of the die pattern on page 86, programmed
   with the numbers *2, 3, 4, 6, 8, 12*
paper

A student chooses a card and, at the top of her paper, writes the number and circles it. Then she rolls the die, writes the number rolled, and circles it. She writes a subtraction problem subtracting the number rolled from the first number. After she completes the problem, she subtracts the number rolled from the difference, as shown, and continues in this manner until she reaches "0." She counts the number of subtraction problems she has written and writes and circles the number at the top of her paper. Then she uses the three circled numbers to write a division sentence. The child repeats the activity as time allows.

## Classy Comparisons

### Fractions

**Materials:**
paper
crayons

A child draws a picture of himself and several of his classmates. Then he writes fractions to describe the attributes of the people he has drawn.

## We Go Together

### Fact families

**Materials:**
12 cards, each labeled with one of the following
   numbers: *3, 7, 21, 6, 9, 54, 2, 8, 16, 4, 5, 20*
paper

A child arranges the cards into four groups so that there are one product and its two factors in each group. Then the child writes on his paper a multiplication fact for each group. Under each fact, he writes the remaining facts in the family, as shown. For an added challenge, program three additional index cards with numbers from another fact family and have the child repeat the activity with 15 cards instead of 12.

## Making Predictions

### Patterns

**Materials:**
colored tiles or paper squares
index cards (one per child)
crayons

A student uses tiles to create a pattern and then copies the pattern on her index card. She writes questions, such as those shown, and then writes the answer to each question.

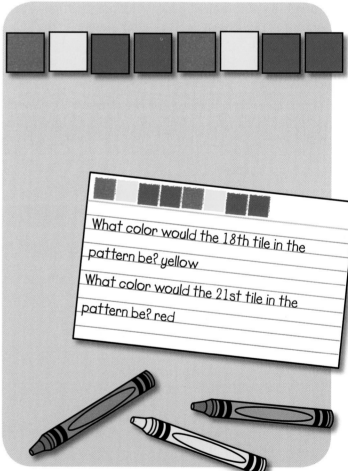

# Parts of Words

## Fractions

**Materials:**
list of spelling words
paper

A child draws on his paper a three-column chart with headings as shown. In the first column, he writes his spelling words. In the remaining columns, he writes a fraction to show what part of the word is vowels and then a fraction to show what part of the word is consonants.

| Word | Vowels | Consonants |
|---|---|---|
| reread | $\frac{3}{6}$ | $\frac{3}{6}$ |
| recheck | $\frac{2}{7}$ | $\frac{5}{7}$ |
| unable | $\frac{3}{6}$ | $\frac{3}{6}$ |
| disrespect | $\frac{3}{10}$ | $\frac{7}{10}$ |

# Linking Numbers

## Multiplication

For partners

**Materials:**
copies of the multiplication table on
    page 100 (one per student)
deck of cards with the face cards removed
2 different-colored highlighters
one black crayon

Explain to the partners that each ace equals one. One partner shuffles the cards and stacks them face-down. In turn, each player flips over the top two cards, multiplies the numbers he has drawn, locates the product on the table, and then highlights the product. Each time a player links three spaces horizontally, vertically, or diagonally, he draws a black line through them and gives himself a point. (Squares connected with black lines may not be used again.) Players play through the deck one time and then count their points. The player with more points is the winner.

## Points on a Line

### Fractions

**Materials:**
1" x 9" construction paper strips (two per child)
construction paper
glue
ruler

A student folds a strip in half and then folds it again so that it is divided into four equal sections. He labels each section "1/4," and then glues the strip on his paper to form a fraction bar, as shown. Then he uses a ruler to draw a number line across the top of the bar. Using the fraction bar as a guide, he labels the points on the number line. He repeats the steps, folding a strip into six equal sections instead of four, and labeling each section "1/6," as shown. He writes statements about the two strips.

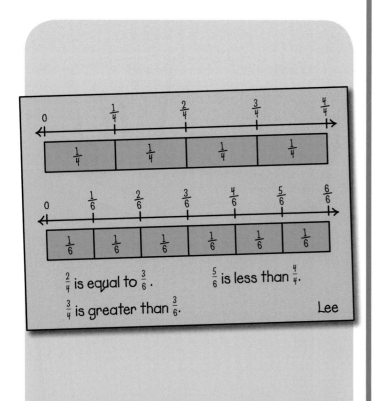

## It All Relates

### Multiplication and division

**Materials:**
multiplication flash cards
colored tiles, counters, or paper squares
paper

A child draws a flash card and then uses tiles to make an array that represents the problem on the card. She writes and solves the multiplication problem, counting the tiles to help her find the product. Then she rearranges the tiles in a number of piles equal to one of the factors. She writes a division problem, using the total number of tiles as her dividend and the number of piles as her divisor. Next, she counts the tiles in a pile to find the quotient. She repeats the activity with a different flash card.

## Three of a Kind?

### Perimeter

**Materials:**
1" graph paper
construction paper

A child cuts a desired shape from the graph paper and then counts the units around the outline of the shape to find its perimeter. Next, she cuts out two more shapes that each have the same perimeter as the first shape, being careful to make shapes that are not congruent to each other or to the first shape. She glues the shapes on her construction paper. Then she writes the perimeter of the three shapes on the paper.

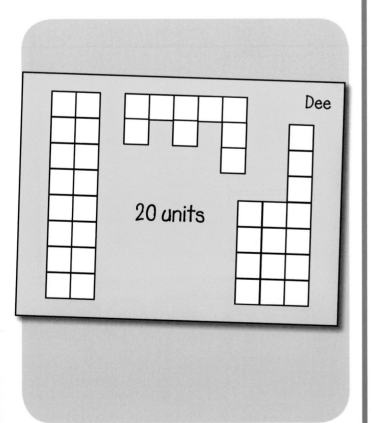

## No Peeking

### Congruence

**Materials:**
10 congruent pairs of die-cut shapes in a paper lunch bag
paper

A student gently shakes the bag and then pulls out one shape. He traces the shape on his paper and lists three of its attributes. Next, without looking, he reaches into the bag and tries to find a shape that is congruent to the first one, referring to his list of attributes to help him. Then he pulls out a shape and, if it is congruent, traces it next to the first one. If it is not congruent, he puts it back in the bag and tries again. He repeats the activity until he has drawn three congruent pairs.

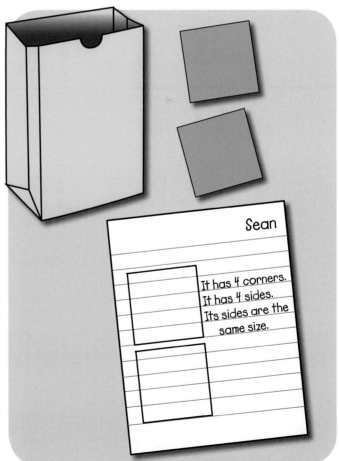

# Set 26

## Mirror Image

### Symmetry

**Materials:**
Geoboard and bands
handheld mirror
ruler
paper

A student uses the bands to make a simple shape on her Geoboard. Then, using her ruler to help her, she draws the shape, flipping it to make the other half of a symmetrical shape. To check her drawing, she holds the mirror next to the Geoboard shape and compares the image to her drawing.

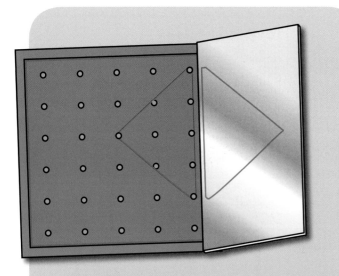

Penny

## Cash and Carry

### Making change

**Materials:**
student copies of page 101
student copies of page 97
money manipulatives
scissors

A student uses the money manipulatives and the cards from page 97 to complete the activity on page 101.

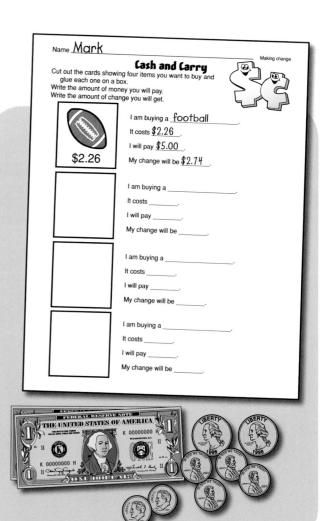

Name **Mark**

**Cash and Carry**
Cut out the cards showing four items you want to buy and glue each one on a box.
Write the amount of money you will pay.
Write the amount of change you will get.

Making change

I am buying a ___football___ .
It costs $2.26 .
I will pay $5.00 .
My change will be $2.74 .

$2.26

I am buying a _____.
It costs _____.
I will pay _____.
My change will be _____.

I am buying a _____.
It costs _____.
I will pay _____.
My change will be _____.

I am buying a _____.
It costs _____.
I will pay _____.
My change will be _____.

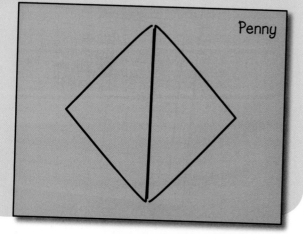

## All About Animals

### Division

**Materials:**
animal picture books
paper

A student chooses a picture and writes a story problem about the animal on it. On the back of the paper, he writes the answer. He repeats the activity as time allows.

Max

1. There are 24 dog legs in the yard. How many dogs are there?

1. 24 ÷ 4 = 6

DOGS

## Go for the Lowest

### Subtraction with regrouping

**For partners**

**Materials:**
copy of page 102, cut apart
card labeled "900"
paper

Each player writes "900" at the top of his paper. One player shuffles the cards, places the deck face-down, and then turns over the top card. He subtracts the number on the card from his 900. His partner turns over the next card and subtracts it from her 900. The player whose difference is lower earns a point. Players continue, each time subtracting from 900, until they have played through the deck. The player who earns more points is the winner.

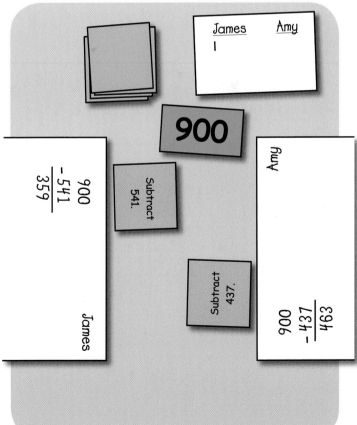

James    Amy
1

900

Subtract 541.

Subtract 437.

$$\begin{array}{r} 900 \\ -541 \\ \hline 359 \end{array}$$

James

$$\begin{array}{r} 900 \\ -437 \\ \hline 463 \end{array}$$

Amy

## Parts of a Whole

### Fractions

**Materials:**
3" construction paper squares (six per child)
construction paper

To make a fraction poster, a child carefully folds her paper squares into fractional parts, as shown. She unfolds each square, draws lines on the fold lines, and labels each fractional part. Then she glues her squares onto a sheet of construction paper. She draws lines to separate the matching fraction squares into sets and then labels each set as shown.

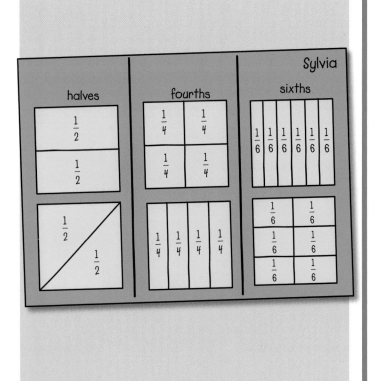

## Zoo Architect

### Perimeter

**Materials:**
animal picture cards
ruler
paper
crayons

A child chooses an animal card and uses his ruler to measure and draw a habitat for the animal. He writes the measurement of each line next to it. He writes the animal's name and the habitat's perimeter, as shown, and then draws and colors animals and details in the habitat. To complete his zoo, he repeats the steps with other animal cards.

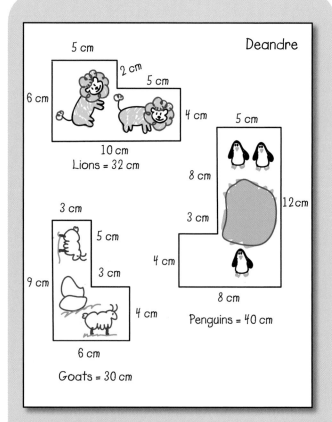

## Writing in Code

### Ordered pairs

**Materials:**
copy of the alphabet grid on page 103
vocabulary list
paper

A child writes on his paper one word from the list and then refers to the grid as he writes the ordered pair for each letter of the word. He repeats the steps for each of the words on the list.

Vocabulary List
together
myself
laugh
clean
drink

Brian

together (5, 4), (6, 6), (4, 8), (2, 1), (5, 4), (2, 4), (2, 1), (8, 3)

myself (0, 2), (6, 2), (8, 0), (2, 1), (2, 6), (4, 0)

Name Brian                          Ordered pairs

## Drawing for Counters

### Fractions

**Materials:**
set of dominoes
40 counters

For partners

Players place the dominoes facedown. One player flips a domino over and takes $\frac{1}{2}$, $\frac{1}{3}$, or $\frac{1}{4}$ of the total number of dots shown on the domino in counters. (If it's impossible for him to take $\frac{1}{2}$, $\frac{1}{3}$, or $\frac{1}{4}$ of the dots shown, his turn is over.) He removes the domino from the game. The second player takes a turn in the same manner. Play continues until one player wins the game by collecting 20 counters.

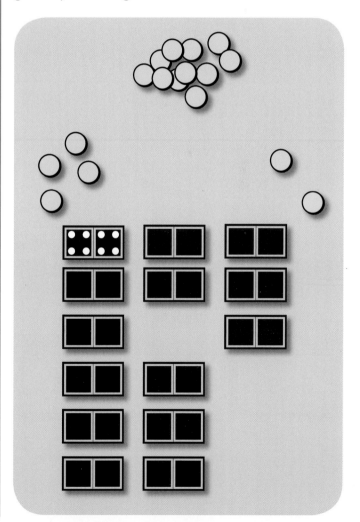

## Flip Over Facts

### Division

**Materials:**
division flash cards in a paper lunch bag
cards labeled with quotients so that each one
   matches one of the flash cards

A student lays the quotient cards faceup in rows. After gently shaking the bag, he draws a flash card. Then he places the flash card below its matching quotient card. He continues with the remaining cards as time allows.

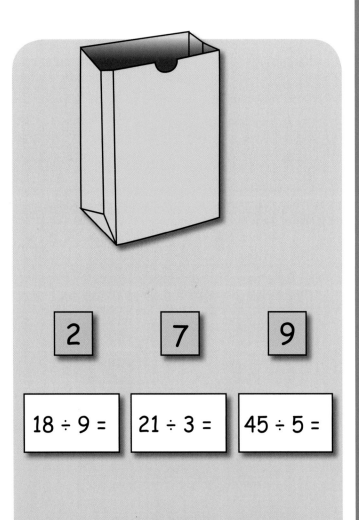

2    7    9

18 ÷ 9 =    21 ÷ 3 =    45 ÷ 5 =

## Colorful Tiling

### Area

**Materials:**
resealable plastic bags, each labeled and filled with a
   different number of colored tiles
paper

A child empties a bag and then uses the tiles to make a shape. He counts the tiles in his shape and then writes the bag's number and the area of the shape on his paper. He repeats the steps with each of the remaining bags.

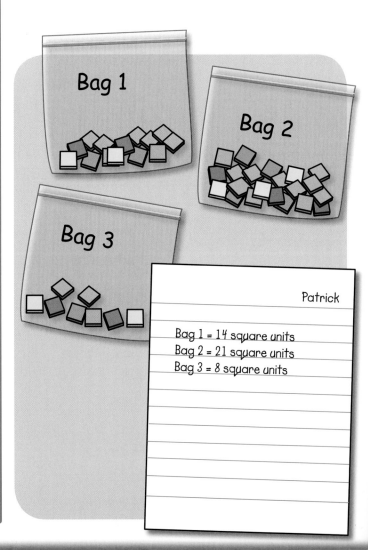

Bag 1
Bag 2
Bag 3

Patrick

Bag 1 = 14 square units
Bag 2 = 21 square units
Bag 3 = 8 square units

## Color the Chances

### Probability

**Materials:**
crayons—4 red, 2 green, 1 yellow
paper lunch bag
1" graph paper
paper
scissors
glue

A child cuts a 3 x 4 grid from the graph paper and then glues the grid on a sheet of paper. He looks at the crayons and then writes predictions about which colors he would pull out if he puts the crayons in the bag and makes 12 pulls. Next, he puts the crayons in the bag, draws one, and uses it to color the first square in his grid. He returns the crayon to the bag and repeats the steps until he has colored each grid square. He finishes the activity by writing about his actual results.

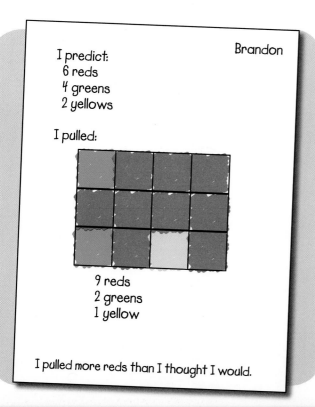

I predict:
6 reds
4 greens
2 yellows

I pulled:

9 reds
2 greens
1 yellow

Brandon

I pulled more reds than I thought I would.

## A Model Comparison

### Fractions

**Materials:**
copy of the fraction cards on page 103, cut apart
fraction bars
paper

A student chooses two of the cards. She uses the fraction bars to make a model of the fraction on each card and then, using the models to help her, writes an inequality sentence on her paper. She repeats the steps as time allows.

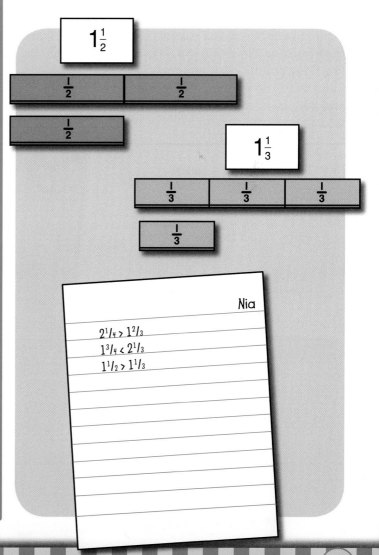

$1\frac{1}{2}$

$\frac{1}{2}$   $\frac{1}{2}$

$\frac{1}{2}$

$1\frac{1}{3}$

$\frac{1}{3}$   $\frac{1}{3}$   $\frac{1}{3}$

$\frac{1}{3}$

Nia

$2\frac{1}{4} > 1\frac{2}{3}$
$1\frac{3}{4} < 2\frac{1}{3}$
$1\frac{1}{2} > 1\frac{1}{3}$

## Rolling for Points

### Addition and subtraction with and without regrouping

**For partners**

**Materials:**
student copies of the recording sheet on page 104
die

One player rolls the die. Then each player writes the rolled number in one of the boxes in the first problem. The players take turns rolling until all six boxes are filled in and then each player solves his problem. The player with the higher sum wins the round. To find the number of points he scores for the first round, he writes, in the boxes at the bottom of the first column, a problem subtracting his partner's sum from his sum. He writes the difference on the "points" line. Play continues through four rounds. To determine the game winner, each player adds his points and the player who scores more points is declared the winner.

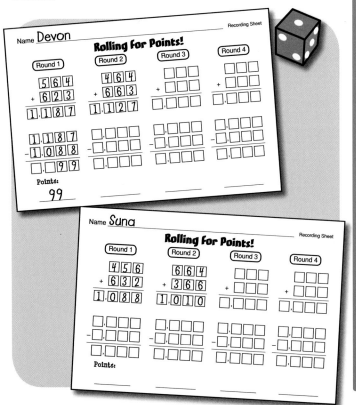

## Careful Comparisons

### Weight

**Materials:**
scale
items to weigh
paper

Possible items include a textbook, stapler, box of tissues, or box of crayons.

A child draws a simple three-column chart with headings like the ones shown. In the first column, she lists the name of each item. In the second column, she writes each item's weight to the nearest pound. Then she compares the weights of the items and writes, in the third column, sentences describing her comparisons.

Tamika

| Item | Weight | Sentence |
|---|---|---|
| book | 4 pounds | The book weighs more than the stapler. |
| stapler | 1 pound | The stapler weighs less than the bottle of water. |
| box of tissues | 1 pound | The box of tissues weighs about the same as the stapler. |
| bottle of water | 2 pounds | The bottle of water weighs more than the box of tissues. |
|  |  |  |

## More or Less

### Fractions

**Materials:**
copy of the fraction cards on page 104, cut apart
fraction bars
die
paper

To make a recording sheet, a child folds his paper into three equal sections, unfolds the paper, and titles the resulting columns as shown. He draws a fraction card, rolls the die, and then takes a number of the drawn fraction bars that matches the number rolled. He writes the fraction he created with the fraction bars in the appropriate column. The child repeats the steps as time allows. For an added challenge, the child trades in fraction bars for wholes, when possible, to make a mixed number. Then he writes the mixed number in the matching column.

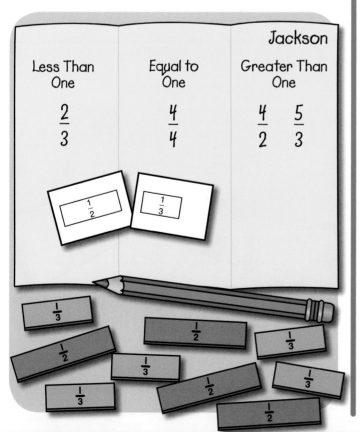

## Balanced on Both Sides

### Symmetry

**Materials:**
construction paper
construction paper scraps
scissors
glue

A student folds a sheet of paper in half lengthwise and then, starting on the fold line, cuts out a paper doll shape. The child folds scrap paper pieces in half and then uses the doll as a pattern to cut out symmetrical clothes and shoes for the doll. He also makes symmetrical hair, facial features, and other details and glues them on his doll.

## In the Pocket

### Fact families

**Materials:**
cards, each programmed with a different product
blank cards
paper

A child chooses a product card and, on each of four blank cards, she writes a different fact that matches the product. She piles the facts on top of the product card. She continues in this way with each of the remaining product cards. Next, she writes each fact family on her paper.

## Shipping and Handling

### Weight

**Materials:**
mailing code, similar to the one shown
store flyers and catalogs
envelopes (two per child)
scissors
crayons

A child draws a red stamp on one envelope and a blue stamp on another. Then she searches through the catalogs or store flyers, cutting out pictures of various objects. She uses the mailing code to help her as she places each picture in the matching envelope.

**Mailing Code**
should be weighed in grams = red
should be weighed in kilograms = blue

## Name the Chances

### Probability

**Materials:**
student copies of page 105
class list

A child uses the names of her classmates to complete the activity.

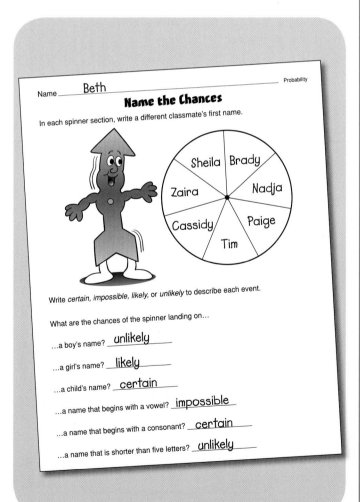

## Dotty Comparisons

### Fractions

**Materials:**
dominoes in a bag
fraction bars
paper

A student draws three dominoes out of the bag and turns each one vertically so that the largest number of dots is on the bottom. He writes the dot sets as fractions on his paper and then uses the fraction bars to model each one. Then he refers to the models as he writes the fractions in order from least to greatest, writing any equivalent fractions next to each other as shown. He repeats the activity with different dominoes as time allows. For an added challenge, the child uses five dominoes instead of three.

## Find a Factor

### Multiplication

**For partners**

**Materials:**
copy of the product cards on page 106,
  cut apart and placed in a cup
copies of the gameboards on page 106 (1 board per child)
scissors

Each player cuts out a gameboard and writes a different digit, 1–9, in each box. Then one player draws a product card and names a fact that equals the product. He looks at his gameboard and crosses out one factor in the fact he has named. The second player takes a turn in the same manner. If a player cannot cross out a factor, his turn is over. Play continues until one player has crossed out all the factors on his board and is declared the winner.

## Stamp It!

### Flips, slides, and turns

**Materials:**
copy of the die pattern on page 86, programmed
  *flip, slide, turn, flip, slide, turn*
rubber stamps
ink pads
paper

A student positions her paper horizontally and then stamps an image in the top left corner of her paper. She rolls the die and follows the direction rolled as she stamps the next image in the row as shown. She labels the second image accordingly and then continues in this manner until the row is completed. She chooses another stamp and repeats the steps as desired.

## Bar to Bar

### Fractions

**Materials:**
copy of page 107, cut apart
bowl
paper

A student puts the cards in the bowl, gently shakes it, and then draws out two cards. On her paper, she writes a fraction that represents the shaded part of each card; then she writes the appropriate inequality symbol between the two fractions. She sets the cards aside and then repeats the steps until she has used all the cards.

Cara

$\frac{1}{4}$ > $\frac{1}{5}$

$\frac{2}{3}$ < $\frac{7}{8}$

## Toss 'Em

### Probability

For partners

**Materials:**
list of 10 fractions similar to the one shown
10 two-sided counters in a cup
paper

Each partner draws a tally table with five rows as shown. In turn, each partner chooses a different fraction from the list and writes it on his table until his table is complete. One partner shakes the cup, pours out the counters, and names the fraction of counters that are red side up. The partner who chose the named fraction makes a mark on his table. Partners continue taking turns until each player has had five turns. Then each partner studies the charts and writes to explain what he notices about them.

Fraction List
$\frac{1}{10}$
$\frac{2}{10}$
$\frac{3}{10}$
$\frac{4}{10}$
$\frac{5}{10}$
$\frac{6}{10}$
$\frac{7}{10}$
$\frac{8}{10}$
$\frac{9}{10}$
$\frac{10}{10}$

| Fraction | Tallies |
|----------|---------|
| $\frac{1}{10}$ | |
| $\frac{4}{10}$ | II |
| $\frac{6}{10}$ | |
| $\frac{7}{10}$ | III |
| $\frac{10}{10}$ | |

$\frac{1}{10}$ and $\frac{10}{10}$ didn't show up at all. $\frac{4}{10}$, $\frac{5}{10}$, and $\frac{6}{10}$ were thrown the most.

| Fraction | Tallies |
|----------|---------|
| $\frac{2}{10}$ | |
| $\frac{3}{10}$ | II |
| $\frac{5}{10}$ | III |
| $\frac{8}{10}$ | |
| $\frac{9}{10}$ | |

$\frac{2}{10}$ wasn't thrown at all. $\frac{5}{10}$ was thrown the most.

## Quick Conversions

### Capacity

**Materials:**
student copies of page 108
scissors

A child cuts apart her copy of the booklet pages and then cuts each page along the bold lines. Next, she stacks one side of the booklet from largest unit to smallest and then staples it along the border. Then she assembles the other half of the booklet in the same manner. The child uses the assembled booklet to help her study capacity units.

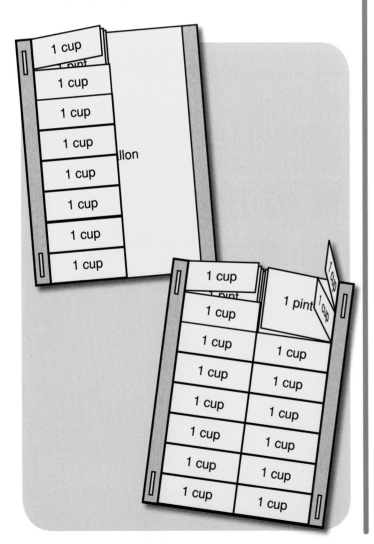

## Clip It!

### Fractions

**Materials:**
copy of page 107, cut apart, each card
    glued to a different clothespin
2½" x 10" poster board strip
fraction bars
paper

A student chooses five clothespins and, using the fraction bars to help her, arranges them in order from least to greatest. (She places any equal fractions next to each other as shown). Then she clips the clothespins onto the poster board strip and writes the fractions in order on her paper. She repeats the steps as time allows.

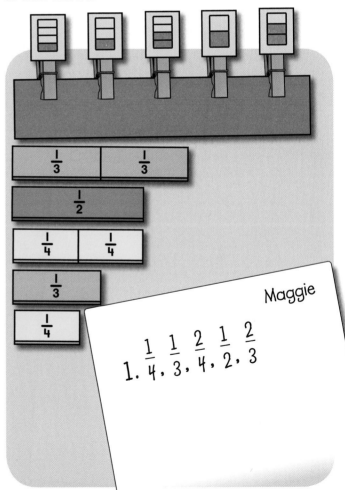

# Home, Sweet Home

## Fact families

**Materials:**
2 sets of 9 cards, each set of cards labeled
   with a different number 1–9
graph paper
crayons

A student shuffles the cards, places the deck face-down, and then turns over the top two cards. She writes on her graph paper a multiplication fact, using the drawn numbers as her factors. Next to the fact, she draws an array that matches it and then decorates the array to make it look like a house as shown. Finally, she writes the remaining facts in the family. She continues in this manner as time allows.

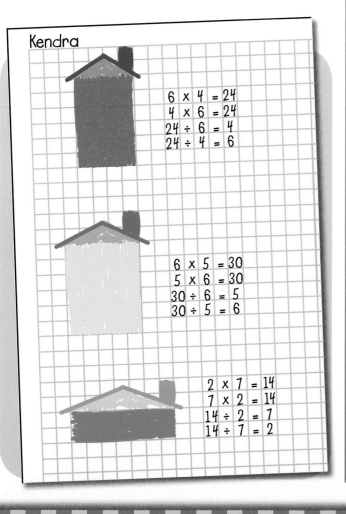

# Furry, Finny Friends

## Graphs

**Materials:**
tally chart of students' pets
1" graph paper

A child chooses a symbol for her graph and writes a graph key at the bottom of her page. Then she refers to the tally chart as she makes her picture graph. On the back of her paper, she writes three facts about her graph.

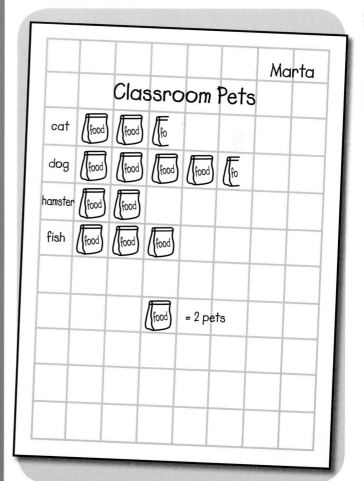

## Take It Away

### Subtraction with and without regrouping

**Materials:**
2 copies of the die pattern on page 86, assembled; one labeled in red with the numbers *548, 679, 758, 792, 850, 926;* one labeled in blue with the numbers *105, 142, 247, 320, 372, 418*
paper

A child rolls the dice and writes on his paper a subtraction problem using the number from the red die on the top and the number from the blue die on the bottom. He solves the problem and then repeats the steps as time allows.

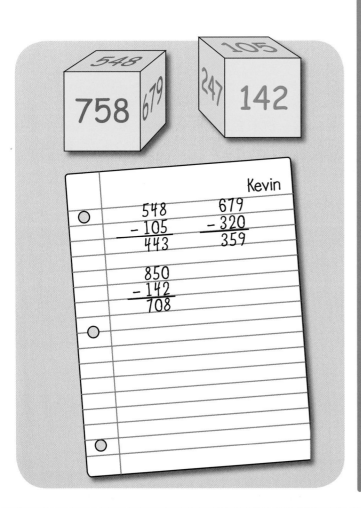

## Soft Grab

### Graphs

**Materials:**
paper lunch bag half-filled with pom-poms in four colors
1" graph paper
crayons
paper

A student reaches into the bag, grabs a handful of pom-poms, and then sorts her handful into four piles according to color. On the graph paper, she makes a bar graph displaying the results of her sort, labeling and titling her graph as shown. Then, on another sheet of paper, she writes and answers questions about her graph.

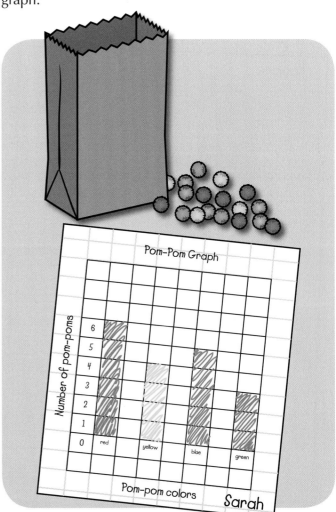

## Factors on a Stick

### Multiplication

**Materials:**
10 craft sticks, each labeled with a different
      number from 0–9
cup
paper

A student places the sticks number-side down in the cup. He gently shakes the cup and pulls out two sticks. Then he writes on his paper the numbers he pulled as factors in a multiplication problem and solves the problem. He returns the sticks to the cup and repeats the activity as time allows. For an added challenge, label each stick with a different dividend; then have the child pull one stick and write a division fact using the dividend.

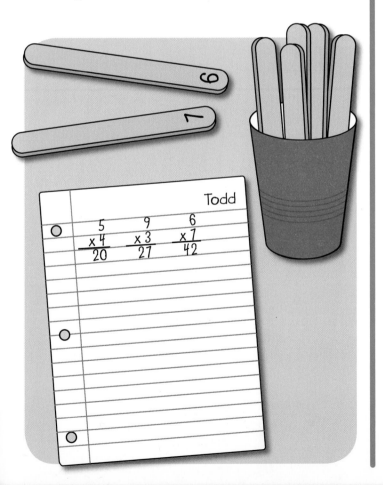

## Find a Rule

### Tables

**Materials:**
cards labeled with number clues similar to those shown
1" graph paper
scissors
glue
paper

A child chooses a card and then makes a two-row table on her graph paper, starting in the top row with one of the items that is described on the card and then increasing the number by one in each column of that row. She completes the table by filling in the second row, as shown; then she cuts out the table and glues it on her paper. Below the table, she writes the rule, as shown. She repeats the steps with each of the remaining cards.

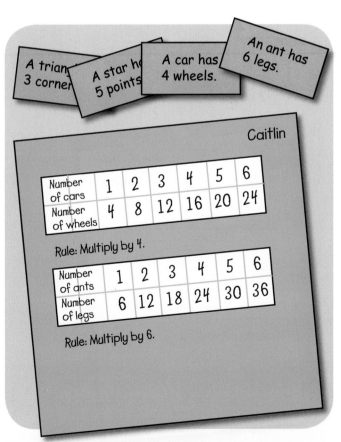

## How Heavy?

### Weight

**Materials:**
scale
paper
paper cups, each partially filled with a different
    measurable item

> Possible items include rocks, paper clips, pennies,
> pom-poms, and cotton balls.

A child examines the cups and predicts the order of the cups by weight by writing a list of the items in the cups from lightest to heaviest. Then she weighs each item and checks the actual order against her prediction. She lists the items in the correct order on her paper.

## In the Spider's Web

### Addition with and without regrouping

**Materials:**
student copies of a spiderweb, as shown
9 or more cards, each labeled with a 2-digit number

A child chooses eight cards and writes their numbers in the center sections of her web. Then she chooses a ninth card and writes its number at the bottom of the page. She adds the number to each number in the web, writing the sum in the next section, as shown. Then she adds the number to each new number, writing the sums in the outside sections to complete the web. For an added challenge, have the child repeat the activity with a three-digit number in each center section of her web.

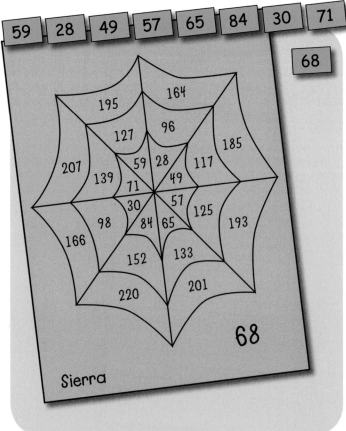

## Make a Trade

### Counting coins

**Materials:**
money manipulatives
coin code, similar to the one shown
pair of dice
paper

For partners

Each player creates on his paper a six-column chart with headings as shown. In turn, each player rolls a die and refers to the coin code. He takes the coins he has rolled and places them on his chart. If a child can, he trades coin sets of equal value to get the least number of coins. After all possible trades have been made, players count their money and the player with the bigger amount is declared the winner.

**Coin Code**
1 = penny
2 = nickel
3 = dime
4 = quarter
5 = half-dollar
6 = dollar

## Folding and Finding

### Fractions

**Materials:**
paper strip folded into sixths
cards labeled with the fractions shown
paper strips
crayons
paper

A child selects a fraction card and then folds a strip to divide it into the same number of parts as the fraction's denominator. Then he colors the same number of parts as the fraction's numerator. Next, he selects another card and folds a second strip to match the model. Then he writes on his paper an equation that represents the drawings. He repeats the steps with each remaining card.

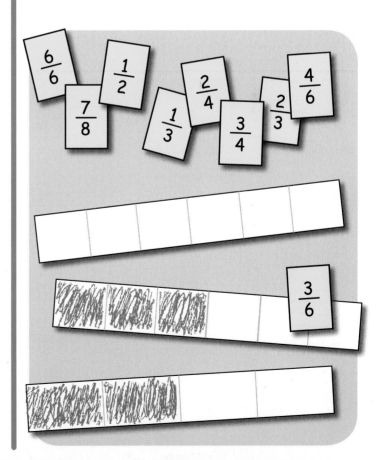

## Greedy!

### Addition with and without regrouping

For partners

**Materials:**
3 wooden blocks, each labeled with the following
   numbers: *0, 1, 2, 3, 4, 5*
paper

One player rolls the blocks and then decides
whether to keep his numbers or to keep rolling in
hopes of rolling larger numbers. If he keeps the
numbers, he arranges them into the largest possible
number and writes it on his paper. If he keeps rolling,
he rolls all three cubes until he decides to keep the
numbers. If he rolls a "0," he must stop rolling and
write "0" for that roll. Each player, in turn, rolls until
he has written three numbers. Then each player adds
his numbers and the player with the larger sum is
declared the winner.

## A House Built of Straw

### Perimeter

**Materials:**
drinking straws cut into various lengths
ruler
paper

A child arranges several straws into a house
outline, estimates the perimeter of the house, and
writes it on his paper. He uses his ruler to measure
each side of the house, writing the measurements as
he works. Then he adds the measurements to find the
actual perimeter of the house. He compares his estimate to the actual perimeter and repeats the steps as
time allows.

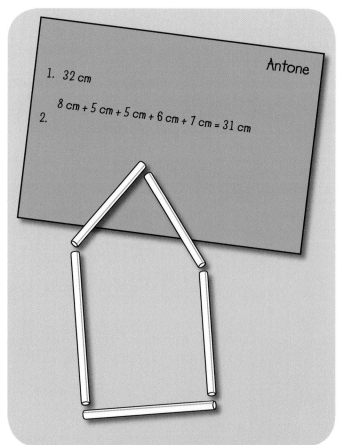

## Cash Giveaway

### Subtracting money

**Materials:**
copy of page 109, assembled
paper

A student slides the strips through the viewer and uses the numbers to write different subtraction problems on his paper. After he has solved a predetermined number of problems, he replaces strip B with strip C and repeats the steps.

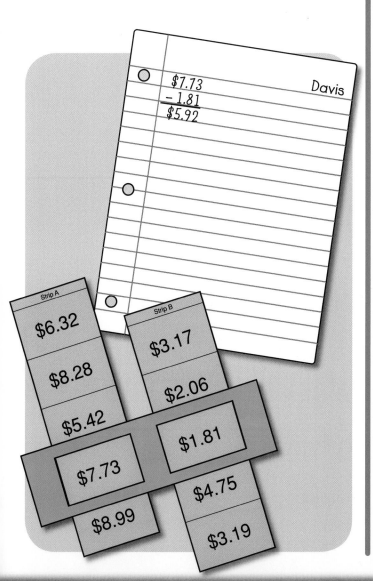

## Shake and Solve

### Multiplication

**Materials:**
clean, empty 20-ounce water bottle
4 dice, 3 of one color and 1 of another,
    stored inside the water bottle
paper

A child shakes the bottle and lays it on its side. Then she writes a multiplication problem using the numbers represented on the three like-colored dice as the top factor and the number represented on the other die as the bottom factor. She solves the problem and then repeats the steps until she has written and solved a predetermined number of problems.

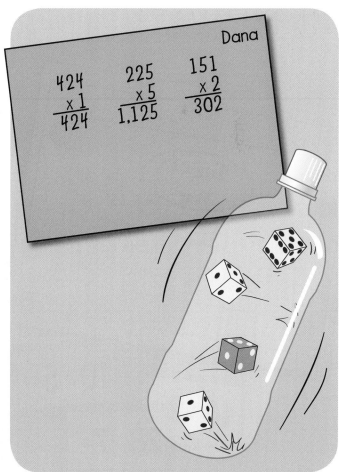

## Tug of War

### Division

For partners

**Materials:**
copy of page 110
2 game markers
division flash cards
coin

Each partner places his game marker on Start and chooses a different direction to travel on the game-board. To begin play, one partner draws a card and solves the problem. If his answer is correct, he flips the coin and refers to the coin code on the board as he moves his game marker on his side of the path. If his answer is incorrect, his turn is over. Then his partner takes a turn in a similar manner. Play continues until one player crosses Finish and is declared the winner.

## Deal a Number

### Expanded notation

**Materials:**
two 9" x 12" sheets of construction paper, each folded, stapled, and labeled to make three pockets as shown
twenty ½" x 6" cards, each labeled on one end with a different number from 0–9
paper

A student places the folded pockets side by side and then deals one card into each pocket. She copies the number she made onto her paper and writes the expanded form of the number. She removes the cards and repeats the steps until she has written a predetermined number of problems.

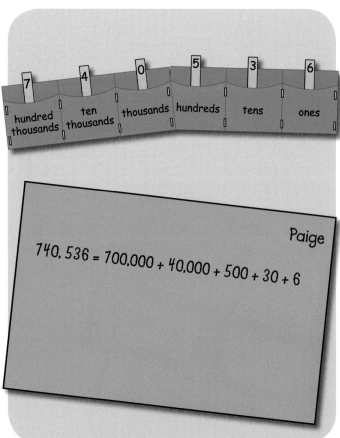

## All in a Line

### Graphs

**Materials:**
class list
12" x 18" paper with a number line drawn at the bottom, similar to the one shown
counters
paper

A student counts the letters in each classmate's name and then places a counter above each matching number on the line plot. Then she makes a tally chart that shows the result of her line plot.

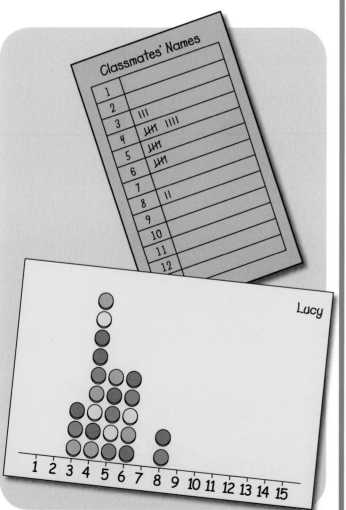

## Deal and Roll

### Multiplication

**Materials:**
copy of the number cards on page 83, cut apart
die
paper

A child shuffles the cards, stacks them facedown, and turns over the top card. She rolls the die and then writes a problem on her paper, multiplying the two-digit number from the card by the one-digit number on the die. She solves the problem and then repeats the steps until she has written a predetermined number of problems.

# Day by Day

Answer the questions.

1. What is the name of the month? _____

2. How many days are in the month? _____

3. How many Mondays are in the month? _____

4. How many Fridays are in the month? _____

5. How many weekdays are in the month? _____

6. How many weekend days are in the month? _____

7. What is the date of the second Sunday? _____

8. What is the date of the third Thursday? _____

9. What is the name of the day that is on the 18th? _____

10. What is the name of the day that is on the 3rd? _____

11. What is today's date? _____

12. What will the date be tomorrow? _____

Super Simple Independent Practice: Math • ©The Mailbox® Books • TEC61156

**76**  **Note to the teacher:** Use with "Day by Day" on page 5.

Use with "Card Connections" on page 6, "A Home for Numbers" on page 12, "Places, Please!" on page 14, "Quick Compare" on page 16, "Which Is Greater?" on page 19, and "Roll One, Draw One" on page 39.

| | | | | |
|---|---|---|---|---|
| 0 | 1 | 2 | 3 | 4 |
| TEC61156 | TEC61156 | TEC61156 | TEC61156 | TEC61156 |
| 5 | 6 | 7 | 8 | 9 |
| TEC61156 | TEC61156 | TEC61156 | TEC61156 | TEC61156 |

## Higher Number Cards

Use with "Card Connections" on page 6.

| | | | | |
|---|---|---|---|---|
| 10 | 11 | 12 | 13 | 14 |
| TEC61156 | TEC61156 | TEC61156 | TEC61156 | TEC61156 |
| 15 | 16 | 17 | 18 | 19 |
| TEC61156 | TEC61156 | TEC61156 | TEC61156 | TEC61156 |

# Clock Patterns

Use with "During My Day" on page 7 and "Rolling Along" on page 10.

# Hundred Chart

Use with "Four in a Row" on page 10 and "Dealing and Adding" on page 15.

| 1 | 2 | 3 | 4 | 5 | 6 | 7 | 8 | 9 | 10 |
|---|---|---|---|---|---|---|---|---|----|
| 11 | 12 | 13 | 14 | 15 | 16 | 17 | 18 | 19 | 20 |
| 21 | 22 | 23 | 24 | 25 | 26 | 27 | 28 | 29 | 30 |
| 31 | 32 | 33 | 34 | 35 | 36 | 37 | 38 | 39 | 40 |
| 41 | 42 | 43 | 44 | 45 | 46 | 47 | 48 | 49 | 50 |
| 51 | 52 | 53 | 54 | 55 | 56 | 57 | 58 | 59 | 60 |
| 61 | 62 | 63 | 64 | 65 | 66 | 67 | 68 | 69 | 70 |
| 71 | 72 | 73 | 74 | 75 | 76 | 77 | 78 | 79 | 80 |
| 81 | 82 | 83 | 84 | 85 | 86 | 87 | 88 | 89 | 90 |
| 91 | 92 | 93 | 94 | 95 | 96 | 97 | 98 | 99 | 100 |

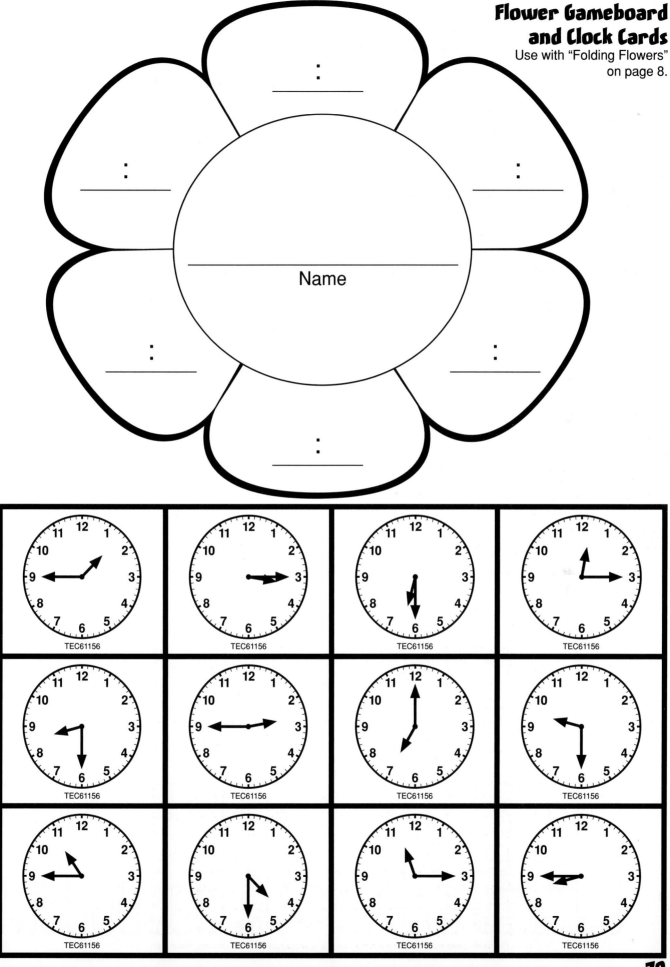

# Place-Value Block Patterns

Use with "Two Views" on page 11.

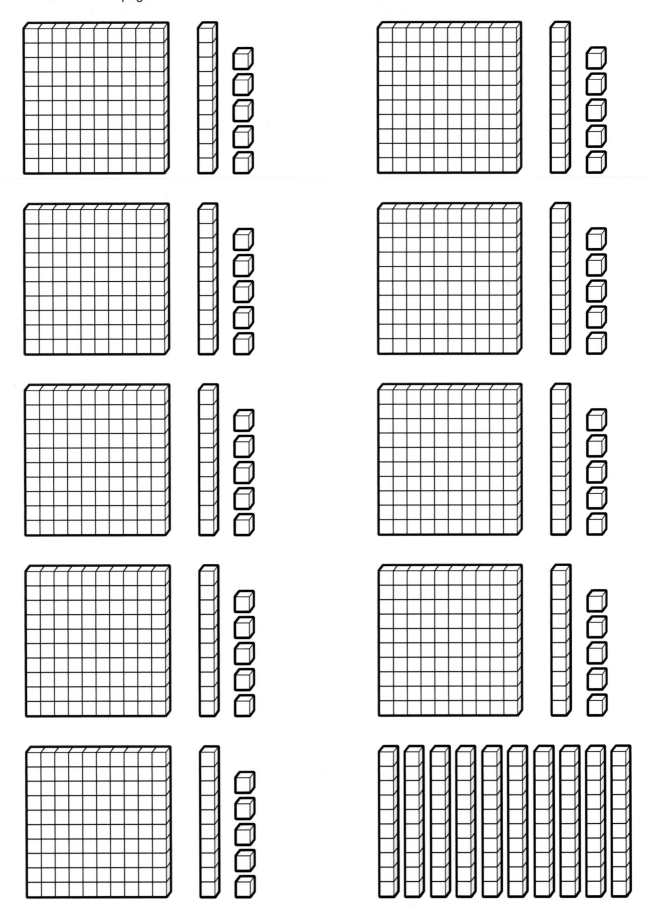

*Super Simple Independent Practice: Math* • ©The Mailbox® Books • TEC61156

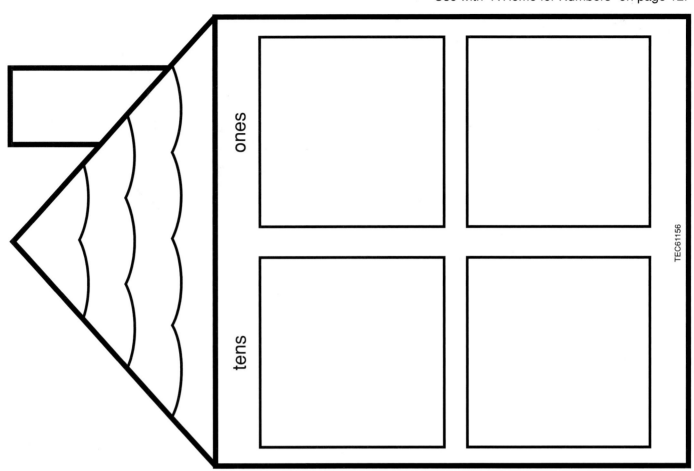

ones

tens

TEC61156

| Birthday Tally Chart | | | |
|---|---|---|---|
| January | | July | |
| February | | August | |
| March | | September | |
| April | | October | |
| May | | November | |
| June | | December | |

*Super Simple Independent Practice: Math* • ©The Mailbox® Books • TEC61156

**Note to the teacher:** Use with "Classy Birthdays" on page 14.

**81**

# Class Birthdays

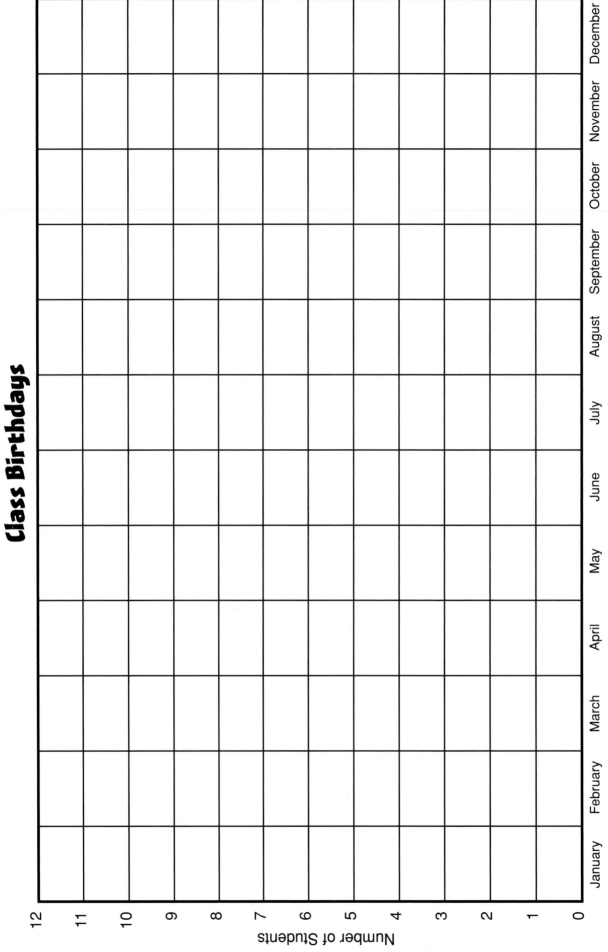

| Number of Students | January | February | March | April | May | June | July | August | September | October | November | December |
|---|---|---|---|---|---|---|---|---|---|---|---|---|
| 12 | | | | | | | | | | | | |
| 11 | | | | | | | | | | | | |
| 10 | | | | | | | | | | | | |
| 9 | | | | | | | | | | | | |
| 8 | | | | | | | | | | | | |
| 7 | | | | | | | | | | | | |
| 6 | | | | | | | | | | | | |
| 5 | | | | | | | | | | | | |
| 4 | | | | | | | | | | | | |
| 3 | | | | | | | | | | | | |
| 2 | | | | | | | | | | | | |
| 1 | | | | | | | | | | | | |
| 0 | | | | | | | | | | | | |

Months of the Year

*Super Simple Independent Practice: Math* • ©The Mailbox® Books • TEC61156

**Note to the teacher:** Use with "Classy Birthdays" on page 14.

| | | | |
|---|---|---|---|
| 38<br>TEC61156 | 51<br>TEC61156 | 36<br>TEC61156 | 29<br>TEC61156 |
| 46<br>TEC61156 | 23<br>TEC61156 | 14<br>TEC61156 | 18<br>TEC61156 |
| 27<br>TEC61156 | 11<br>TEC61156 | 57<br>TEC61156 | 45<br>TEC61156 |
| 52<br>TEC61156 | 48<br>TEC61156 | 49<br>TEC61156 | 33<br>TEC61156 |

# Tens Cards
Use with "Dealing and Adding" on page 15.

| | | | |
|---|---|---|---|
| 10<br>TEC61156 | 20<br>TEC61156 | 30<br>TEC61156 | 40<br>TEC61156 |
| 10<br>TEC61156 | 20<br>TEC61156 | 30<br>TEC61156 | 40<br>TEC61156 |

## Place Value Mat

Use with "Quick Compare" on page 16 and "Which Is Greater?" on page 19.

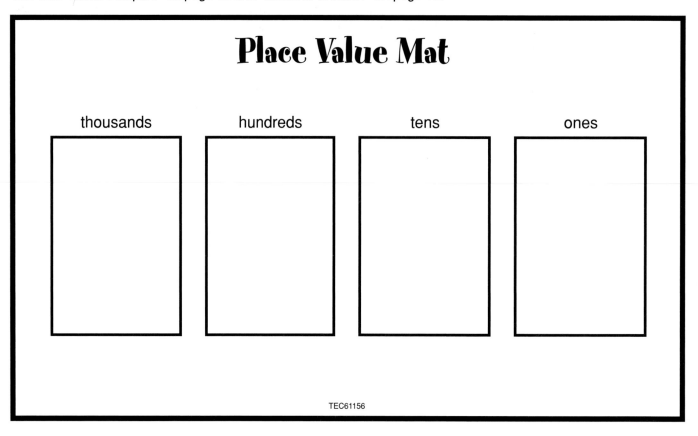

# Place Value Mat

| thousands | hundreds | tens | ones |

TEC61156

## Task Cards

Use with "Tackling Tasks" on page 17.

Write your full name six times.

TEC61156

Write the months of the year two times.

TEC61156

Open a book and read three pages.

TEC61156

Roll a die until you roll a six.

TEC61156

Write three sentences about your favorite food.

TEC61156

Write the numbers from 1 to 100.

TEC61156

# Spinner Pattern

Use with "Up or Down?" on page 20, "Spin Again!" on page 24, "Spin the Difference" on page 32, "Facts All Around" on page 33, and "Mystery Number" on page 46.

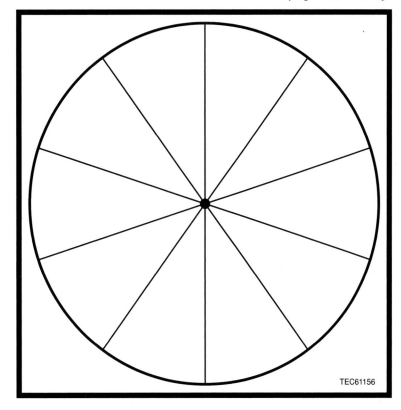

TEC61156

# Flash Cards

Use with "Model Problems" on page 22.

| 530<br>+ 241 | 261<br>+ 411 | 321<br>+ 373 | 214<br>+ 160 | 321<br>+ 534 | 842<br>+ 132 |
|---|---|---|---|---|---|
| TEC61156 | TEC61156 | TEC61156 | TEC61156 | TEC61156 | TEC61156 |
| 305<br>+ 264 | 597<br>+ 301 | 211<br>+ 572 | 460<br>+ 123 | 412<br>+ 456 | 354<br>+ 102 |
| TEC61156 | TEC61156 | TEC61156 | TEC61156 | TEC61156 | TEC61156 |
| 520<br>+ 105 | 125<br>+ 832 | 143<br>+ 346 | 762<br>+ 212 | 534<br>+ 145 | 160<br>+ 737 |
| TEC61156 | TEC61156 | TEC61156 | TEC61156 | TEC61156 | TEC61156 |

# Die Pattern

Use with "Rolling for Shapes" on page 21, "Rolling for Cash" on page 40, "Roll and Measure" on page 44, "Subtract Again" on page 49, "Stamp It!" on page 64, and "Take It Away" on page 68.

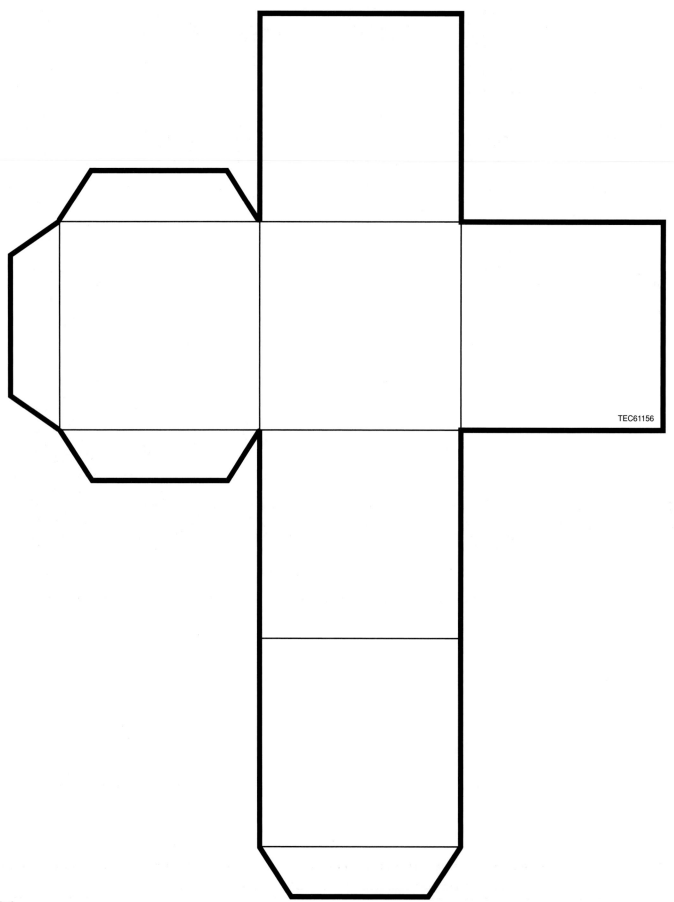

TEC61156

*Super Simple Independent Practice: Math* • ©The Mailbox® Books • TEC61156

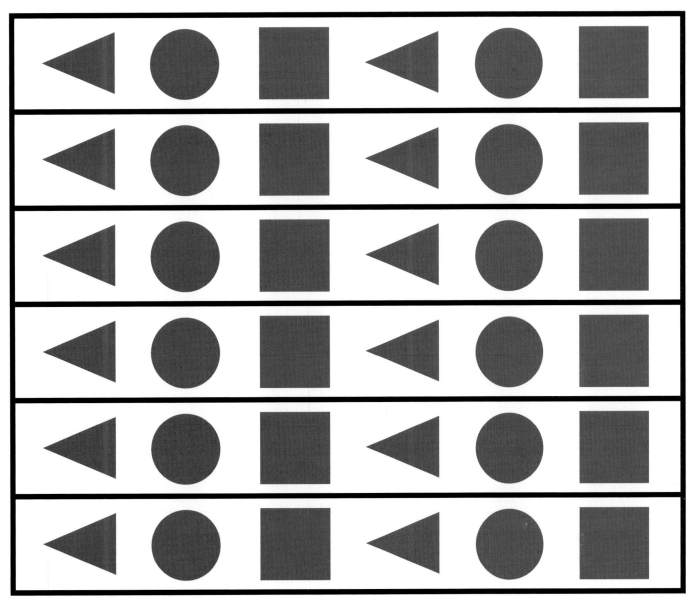

**Note to the teacher:** Cut out the viewer and then cut along the dotted lines. Cut out the pattern strips and thread them through the viewer.

# Expanded Notation Gameboards

Use with "Spin Again!" on page 24.

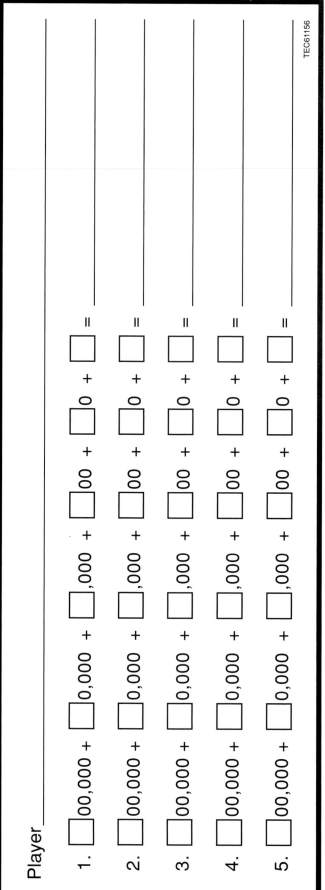

*Super Simple Independent Practice: Math* • ©The Mailbox® Books • TEC61156

# Spinner Pattern

Use with "Spin and Underline" on page 26 and "Mystery Number" on page 46.

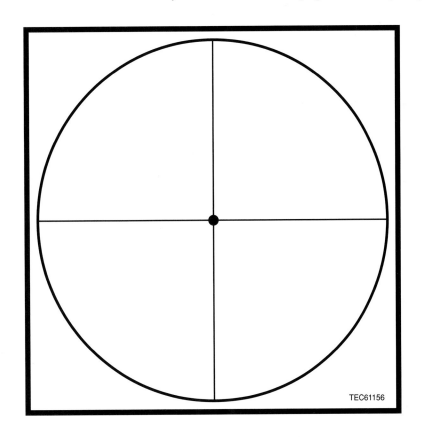

TEC61156

# Thermometer Patterns

Use with "Weather Wear" on page 31.

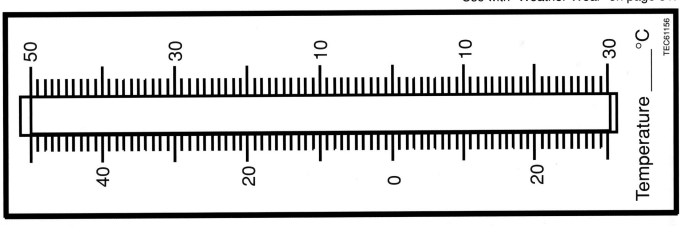

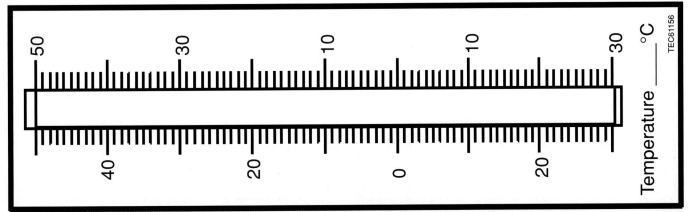

# Thermometer Pattern, Strip Pattern, and Thermometer Cards

Use with "How Hot? How Cold?" on page 26.

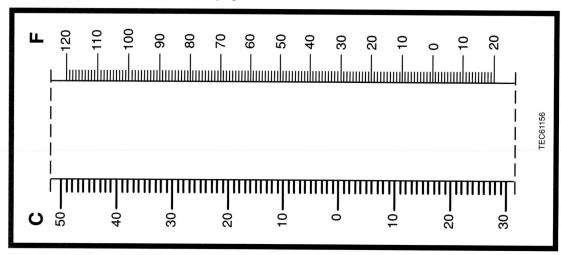

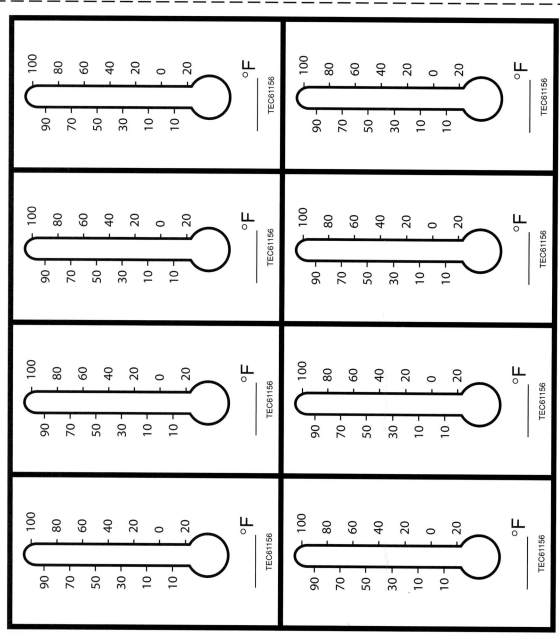

*Super Simple Independent Practice: Math* • ©The Mailbox® Books • TEC61156

Name _____

# What's in a Shape?

Write the name of the shape you modeled.
Draw the shapes you make.
Write their names.

Red shape: _____

• • • • •

• • • • •

• • • • •

• • • • •

• • • • •

Green shapes I made: _____

_____

_____

Red shape: _____

• • • • •

• • • • •

• • • • •

• • • • •

• • • • •

Green shapes I made: _____

_____

_____

Red shape: _____

• • • • •

• • • • •

• • • • •

• • • • •

• • • • •

Green shapes I made: _____

_____

_____

Red shape: _____

• • • • •

• • • • •

• • • • •

• • • • •

• • • • •

Green shapes I made: _____

_____

_____

| FINISH | FINISH |
|--------|--------|
| 10 | 10 |
| 9 | 9 |
| 8 | 8 |
| 7 | 7 |
| 6 | 6 |
| 5 | 5 |
| 4 | 4 |
| 3 | 3 |
| 2 | 2 |
| 1 | 1 |
| START | START |

**Note to the teacher:** Use with "Spin the Difference" on page 32 and "Big Spender" on page 39.

# Facts All Around

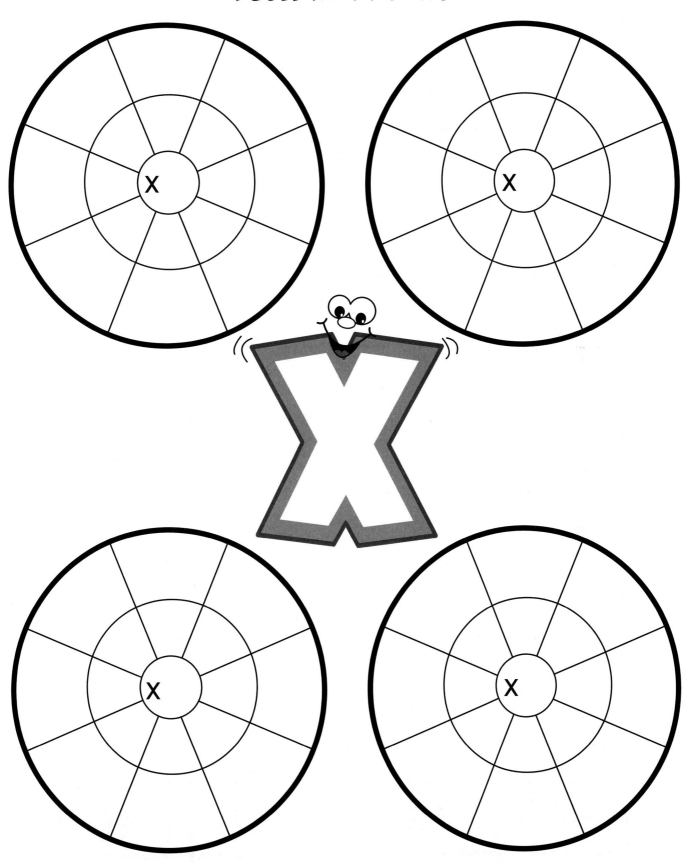

*Super Simple Independent Practice: Math* • ©The Mailbox® Books • TEC61156

**Note to the teacher:** Use with "Facts All Around" on page 33.

93

# Fruity Flavors

Cut apart the spinner pieces below.
Glue one piece in each section of the spinners.

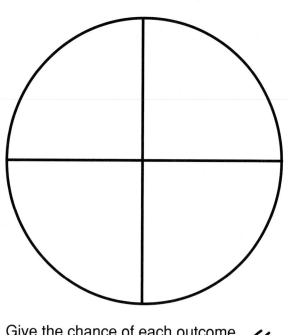

Give the chance of each outcome.

1. apple      ___ out of ___

2. cherry     ___ out of ___

3. lemon     ___ out of ___

4. peach     ___ out of ___

Give the chance of each outcome.

5. apple      ___ out of ___

6. cherry     ___ out of ___

7. lemon     ___ out of ___

8. peach     ___ out of ___

*Super Simple Independent Practice: Math* • ©The Mailbox® Books • TEC61156

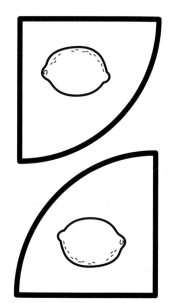

**Note to the teacher:** Use with "Fruity Flavors" on page 35.

| A | 721 | B | 544 |
| A | 940 | B | 243 |
| A | 638 | B | 381 |
| A | 816 | B | 190 |
| A | 552 | B | 409 |
| A | 624 | B | 347 |
| A | 933 | B | 280 |
| A | 758 | B | 463 |
| A | 841 | B | 155 |

TEC61156

| Word | Tally Marks | Frequency |
|---|---|---|
|  |  |  |
|  |  |  |
|  |  |  |
|  |  |  |
|  |  |  |
|  |  |  |
|  |  |  |
|  |  |  |
|  |  |  |
|  |  |  |
|  |  |  |
|  |  |  |
|  |  |  |
|  |  |  |

**Note to the teacher:** Use with "Counting on Letters" on page 38.

Use with "Big Spender" on page 39, "Spending Spree" on page 42, and "Cash and Carry" on page 54.

# Coin Cards

Use with "Rolling for Cash" on page 40.

TEC61156

TEC61156

TEC61156

TEC61156

TEC61156

TEC61156

TEC61156

TEC61156

*Super Simple Independent Practice: Math* • ©The Mailbox® Books • TEC61156

---

Standard measurement

# How Long? How Tall?

Write the measurement of each item.
Then write each measurement in inches.
Use the table to help you.

| Feet | 1 | 2 | 3 | 4 | 5 | 6 | 7 | 8 |
|---|---|---|---|---|---|---|---|---|
| Inches | 12 | 24 | 36 | 48 | 60 | 72 | 84 | 96 |

| Item | Measurement | Measurement in Inches |
|---|---|---|
| | | |
| | | |
| | | |
| | | |
| | | |
| | | |

*Super Simple Independent Practice: Math* • ©The Mailbox® Books • TEC61156

**Note to the teacher:** Use with "How Long? How Tall?" on page 41.

# Roll On!

For each problem, roll three dice.
Write each number you roll in a box.
Solve.

7 7 2
− ☐☐☐
‾‾‾‾‾‾

8 1 9
− ☐☐☐
‾‾‾‾‾‾

8 6 4
− ☐☐☐
‾‾‾‾‾‾

9 3 9
− ☐☐☐
‾‾‾‾‾‾

7 6 0
− ☐☐☐
‾‾‾‾‾‾

9 2 5
− ☐☐☐
‾‾‾‾‾‾

7 0 3
− ☐☐☐
‾‾‾‾‾‾

7 8 2
− ☐☐☐
‾‾‾‾‾‾

9 7 5
− ☐☐☐
‾‾‾‾‾‾

8 2 1
− ☐☐☐
‾‾‾‾‾‾

7 9 3
− ☐☐☐
‾‾‾‾‾‾

8 5 0
− ☐☐☐
‾‾‾‾‾‾

7 8 7
− ☐☐☐
‾‾‾‾‾‾

9 9 3
− ☐☐☐
‾‾‾‾‾‾

8 4 2
− ☐☐☐
‾‾‾‾‾‾

8 9 6
− ☐☐☐
‾‾‾‾‾‾

**Note to the teacher:** Use with "Roll On!" on page 43.

# Multiplication Table

Use with "Linking Numbers" on page 51.

| x | 0 | 1 | 2 | 3 | 4 | 5 | 6 | 7 | 8 | 9 |
|---|---|---|---|---|---|---|---|---|---|---|
| 0 | 0 | 0 | 0 | 0 | 0 | 0 | 0 | 0 | 0 | 0 |
| 1 | 0 | 1 | 2 | 3 | 4 | 5 | 6 | 7 | 8 | 9 |
| 2 | 0 | 2 | 4 | 6 | 8 | 10 | 12 | 14 | 16 | 18 |
| 3 | 0 | 3 | 6 | 9 | 12 | 15 | 18 | 21 | 24 | 27 |
| 4 | 0 | 4 | 8 | 12 | 16 | 20 | 24 | 28 | 32 | 36 |
| 5 | 0 | 5 | 10 | 15 | 20 | 25 | 30 | 35 | 40 | 45 |
| 6 | 0 | 6 | 12 | 18 | 24 | 30 | 36 | 42 | 48 | 54 |
| 7 | 0 | 7 | 14 | 21 | 28 | 35 | 42 | 49 | 56 | 63 |
| 8 | 0 | 8 | 16 | 24 | 32 | 40 | 48 | 56 | 64 | 72 |
| 9 | 0 | 9 | 18 | 27 | 36 | 45 | 54 | 63 | 72 | 81 |

*Super Simple Independent Practice: Math* • ©The Mailbox® Books • TEC61156

Name _____

Multiplication

# Rolling for Factors

For each problem, roll the die and write the number in the box. Multiply.

□
x  5

6
x  □

3
x  □

□
x  9

4
x  □

2
x  □

7
x  □

1
x  □

□
x  8

□
x  6

9
x  □

□
x  7

*Super Simple Independent Practice: Math* • ©The Mailbox® Books • TEC61156

**Note to the teacher:** Use with "Rolling for Factors" on page 48.

# Cash and Carry

Cut out the cards showing four items you want to buy and
  glue each one on a box.
Write the amount of money you will pay.
Write the amount of change you will get.

I am buying a _____.

It costs _____.

I will pay _____.

My change will be _____.

I am buying a _____.

It costs _____.

I will pay _____.

My change will be _____.

I am buying a _____.

It costs _____.

I will pay _____.

My change will be _____.

I am buying a _____.

It costs _____.

I will pay _____.

My change will be _____.

Super Simple Independent Practice: Math • ©The Mailbox® Books • TEC61156

**101**

**Note to the teacher:** Use with "Cash and Carry" on page 54.

# Game Cards

Use with "Go for the Lowest" on page 55.

| | | | |
|---|---|---|---|
| Subtract 321. | Subtract 705. | Subtract 634. | Subtract 275. |
| TEC61156 | TEC61156 | TEC61156 | TEC61156 |
| Subtract 124. | Subtract 437. | Subtract 246. | Subtract 635. |
| TEC61156 | TEC61156 | TEC61156 | TEC61156 |
| Subtract 483. | Subtract 272. | Subtract 390. | Subtract 824. |
| TEC61156 | TEC61156 | TEC61156 | TEC61156 |
| Subtract 307. | Subtract 194. | Subtract 248. | Subtract 564. |
| TEC61156 | TEC61156 | TEC61156 | TEC61156 |
| Subtract 404. | Subtract 675. | Subtract 541. | Subtract 109. |
| TEC61156 | TEC61156 | TEC61156 | TEC61156 |

Super Simple Independent Practice: Math • ©The Mailbox® Books • TEC61156

| | | | |
|---|---|---|---|
| $1\frac{1}{2}$ | $1\frac{1}{3}$ | $2\frac{1}{4}$ | $1\frac{2}{3}$ |
| TEC61156 | TEC61156 | TEC61156 | TEC61156 |
| $1\frac{1}{4}$ | $2\frac{1}{3}$ | $1\frac{2}{4}$ | $2\frac{2}{3}$ |
| TEC61156 | TEC61156 | TEC61156 | TEC61156 |
| $2\frac{1}{2}$ | $1\frac{3}{4}$ | $2\frac{3}{4}$ | $2\frac{2}{4}$ |
| TEC61156 | TEC61156 | TEC61156 | TEC61156 |

Name _____ Ordered pairs

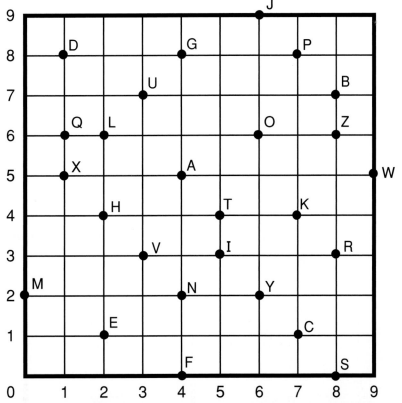

Super Simple Independent Practice: Math • ©The Mailbox® Books • TEC61156

**Note to the teacher:** Use with "Writing in Code" on page 57.

**103**

# Fraction Bar Cards

Use with "More or Less" on page 61.

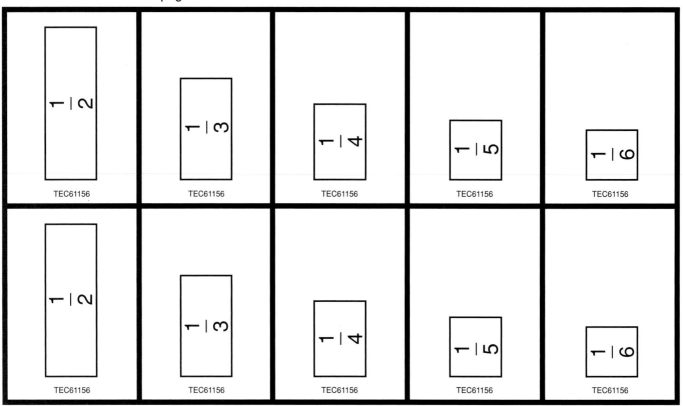

Card grid contents:

Row 1: $\frac{1}{2}$ (TEC61156), $\frac{1}{3}$ (TEC61156), $\frac{1}{4}$ (TEC61156), $\frac{1}{5}$ (TEC61156), $\frac{1}{6}$ (TEC61156)

Row 2: $\frac{1}{2}$ (TEC61156), $\frac{1}{3}$ (TEC61156), $\frac{1}{4}$ (TEC61156), $\frac{1}{5}$ (TEC61156), $\frac{1}{6}$ (TEC61156)

*Super Simple Independent Practice: Math* • ©The Mailbox® Books • TEC61156

Name _____ Recording sheet

# Rolling For Points!

Round 1    Round 2    Round 3    Round 4

□ □ □
+ □ □ □
———————
□ , □ □ □

□ , □ □ □
− □ , □ □ □
———————
□ , □ □ □

Points: _____

*Super Simple Independent Practice: Math* • ©The Mailbox® Books • TEC61156

**Note to the teacher:** Use with "Rolling for Points!" on page 60.

# Name the Chances

In each spinner section, write a different classmate's first name.

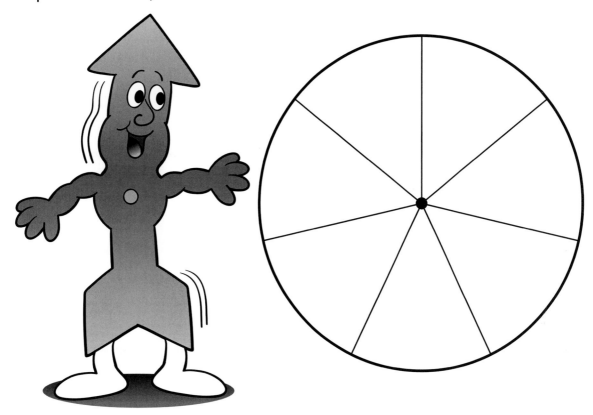

Write *certain, impossible, likely,* or *unlikely* to describe each event.

What are the chances of the spinner landing on…

…a boy's name? _____

…a girl's name? _____

…a child's name? _____

…a name that begins with a vowel? _____

…a name that begins with a consonant? _____

…a name that is shorter than five letters? _____

*Super Simple Independent Practice: Math* • ©The Mailbox® Books • TEC61156

# Product Cards and Gameboards

Use with "Find a Factor" on page 64.

| 1 | 2 | 3 | 4 | 5 | 6 | 7 |
|---|---|---|---|---|---|---|
| 8 | 9 | 10 | 12 | 14 | 16 | 18 |
| 20 | 24 | 25 | 30 | 32 | 35 | 36 |
| 40 | 42 | 45 | 48 | 54 | 63 | 72 |

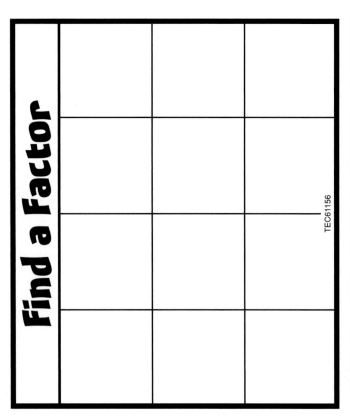

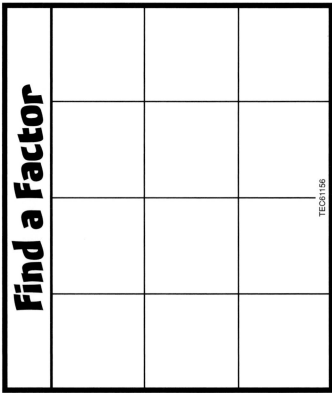

| | | | | |
|---|---|---|---|---|
| TEC61156 | TEC61156 | TEC61156 | TEC61156 | TEC61156 |
| TEC61156 | TEC61156 | TEC61156 | TEC61156 | TEC61156 |
| TEC61156 | TEC61156 | TEC61156 | TEC61156 | TEC61156 |
| TEC61156 | TEC61156 | TEC61156 | TEC61156 | TEC61156 |
| TEC61156 | TEC61156 | TEC61156 | TEC61156 | TEC61156 |

# Capacity Booklet

Use with "Quick Conversions" on page 66.

| 1 gallon | 1 quart | 1 quart |
|---|---|---|

| 1 pint | 1 pint | 1 cup | 1 cup |
|---|---|---|---|
| 1 pint | 1 pint | 1 cup | 1 cup |
| 1 pint | 1 pint | 1 cup | 1 cup |
| 1 pint | 1 pint | 1 cup | 1 cup |
| | | 1 cup | 1 cup |
| | | 1 cup | 1 cup |
| | | 1 cup | 1 cup |
| | | 1 cup | 1 cup |

Super Simple Independent Practice: Math • ©The Mailbox® Books • TEC61156

---

Slot 1                    Slot 2

---

| Strip A | Strip B | Strip C |
|---------|---------|---------|
| $6.32 | $3.17 | $1.40 |
| $8.28 | $2.06 | $2.83 |
| $5.42 | $1.81 | $4.65 |
| $7.73 | $4.75 | $2.11 |
| $8.99 | $3.19 | $4.74 |

*Super Simple Independent Practice: Math* • ©The Mailbox® Books • TEC61156

**Note to the teacher:** Use with "Cash Giveaway" on page 73. Cut out a copy of the viewer and then cut along the dotted lines. Cut out a copy of the strips. Thread strip A through slot 1 and strip B through slot 2. Set strip C aside.

Slip in the mud. Move back one space.

Lose your grip. Move back one space.

Start

Finish

# Tug of War

**Coin Code**
heads = 2 spaces
tails = 1 space

Drop the rope. Move back one space.

Fall on the ground. Move back one space.

*Super Simple Independent Practice: Math* • ©The Mailbox® Books • TEC61156

**Note to the teacher:** Use with "Tug of War" on page 74.

# Skills Index